TOM MUIR'S

Tales of Viking Lands

introduction

"Can we film you in here?" the BBC producer asked as she looked around my sitting room, filled with books and paintings. *"Yeah, sure,"* I said. The lights and camera were set up and my friend, Bella Bathurst, positioned herself nearby to ask the questions. This was for an episode of the BBC2 programme *'Time Watch'*, and was based on Bella's book *'The Wreckers'*, about the illegal looting of wrecked ships. When we finished, the film crew went off to get some more images 'in the can' before they called it a night, leaving Bella at my house, being regaled with stories of shipwreck by my son, who had just had a narrow escape when the creel boat on which he worked had sunk off the island of Papa Westray.

As the story was unfolding, the phone rang. I picked it up and was greeted by a familiar and cheerful voice, *"HELLO! It's the Chief!"* Mats Geschwind (Chief 'Bear Claw'), was the chief at the Storholmen Viking Village in central Sweden, north of Stockholm. Mats was one of Storholmen's founders; it is an educational facility and run as a non-profit-making organisation. *"Tom, we'd like you to come here as our guest of honour. We are having a little feast and we'd like you to join us."*

I was stunned, but also a bit worried. I was going through a bad period in my life, and had lost confidence in most things. I had been a storyteller, but I hadn't done much for two years and had decided that I should probably give it up completely. I explained the situation to Mats, expecting him to withdraw his offer, but instead he said, *"That's OK. We want you to come anyway. We miss you!"* I was moved by his kindness and generosity of spirit; something that he had no lack of. As the weeks slipped past, I thought long and hard about the offer and decided that, if it would help them, then I could tell some stories. I didn't realise it at the time, but this was a hugely important turning point in my life.

I arrived at the village in July, 2007. The people there couldn't have been kinder. I got into Viking clothes and left the 21st century behind for two weeks. I was given a guide who was to show me around and keep an eye on me. She was a tall, beautiful Amazon of a lady called Anna Anglemark (whose surname translates as 'Angel Land'), who has created the artwork for this book. At that time ,she had an arm in a cast, having broken it in a fall a few days before.

We saw the village and the lake on which it lies, and then she took me to see the ancient woodland that surrounds the village, full of oak trees and Viking-Age burial mounds, untouched by archaeologists – a sacred place. We sat on a fallen tree trunk and talked as the sun set, casting golden light all around this beautiful place. I felt like Bilbo Baggins, setting out on a journey to unknown lands. I am not in the habit of wearing Viking clothes for a start! Anna told me of three old oak trees that she called 'the three sisters', and we set off to see them. They were set slightly apart from the rest of the trees, and in front of them was a clearing that leads down to the lake, from which the heavily wooded island of Lillholmen rises from its waters. Lake Erken sparkled with an iridescent light; its very name, in the ancient tongue, means to glitter.

One day, Mats' wife, Britta, commented to me that it was a pity that there were no folk tales about their village. *"There will be by the time that I leave,"* I joked. But one Saturday afternoon, as I sat under those three oak trees, sanding some small pieces of juniper wood that Anna would turn into runes for reading the future, a story started to form in my head. I had not set out to create one; it just invited itself and started to grow. By the time that I had finished, I had a story to give them about their beautiful village, and the breathtaking landscape in which it sits, which I have included in this collection. I had also made up my mind that I would write a book of Nordic folk tales, from all the countries where the Vikings settled. This book, I hoped, would raise some money for them and bring the name of Storholmen to people outside the country.

Every morning, just after breakfast, the lure was blown, and everyone gathered for the morning meeting, to decide who did what that day. There were demonstrations for the visitors of Viking cooking, textile work, blacksmithing, glass bead-making, rune casting and writing, music, song and dance, trips in a Viking boat, a talk on the Swedish Vikings by Mats, a talk on the herbs grown there and used for healing, games and fighting, storytelling for children in Swedish and me telling Orkney stories in the King's Hall. I told different stories every day, to keep it interesting for me. It proved a hit with the numerous kids in the village, who climbed up into the loft room to listen to me. After this morning meeting, Mats would quote, not from Viking literature, but from the old American TV cop show, 'Hill Street Blues', "...and remember; be careful out there!"

I was back there several times after that, and Mats, along with two other friends, came to visit me in Orkney in 2010. He was so inspired by the magnificent hinges on the doors of St Magnus Cathedral that he photographed them, and gave the photo to the village blacksmith, saying "Make me two of those for my house door."

In 2013, I gave Mats a hug at the airport in Stockholm and said that I'd see him again soon. Sadly, that was not meant to be. Mats was diagnosed with cancer soon afterwards and passed away on 25th May, 2014; he was just 53 years old. His widow, Britta, along with her son Alvin and step-son Emil, now run the place. People from all over the world go there to learn, not just about the Viking Age, but about themselves. It is a family, and Mats' death shocked and saddened people very deeply. He is greatly missed by all those people whose lives he touched. He gave me back my stories; he made me want to tell them again. I owe him so much for that. I can never repay the debt.

This book contains folk tales from the Vikings' lands, from places like Scotland where they settled among other people, to Iceland where they colonised an empty land, as well as their heartlands of Denmark, Norway and Sweden. As an Orcadian, writing a book as a gift to my Swedish family, I have reserved the right to include more stories from our two lands – because I can! They are probably not Viking Age, but maybe some of them, in an earlier form, would have been known to the Vikings. They celebrate our shared heritage and will, I hope, find an appreciative audience among modern readers, regardless of where in the world they come from.

Tom Muir

dedication

To my dear, late friend Mats Geschwind (Chief Bear Claw)
and his wonderful family, Britta, Emil and Alvin

"Be careful out there."

FOREWORD

You are travelling in the North, visiting small towns and harbours, country regions, visiting islands and the great tracts of forest and rock-girt seas. In one place there is word of a storyteller, the possibility of a gathering, a session, a small festival even. You are aware, of course, of a huge legacy of stories from saga to folk tales, ghosts to elves, trolls and mermaids, but an actual living storyteller . . . that is something unexpected in the technological era.

Eventually, after much enquiry, direction and redirection, you reach the venue known to locals but little advertised to strangers. Not much seems to be happening, but you are made welcome. You become aware of a shy, rather diffident man somewhere on the fringes. He is neither old nor young, slightly stooped, quiet, yet firmly present, with a keen eye, an attentive tilting head.

Gradually, by some process of undisclosed osmosis, smoothed by oblique introductory hints of something about to come, the diffident man has moved to the centre. This is the storyteller, Tom Muir – from the Orkney Islands, floating north of Scotland.

There is a warmth to the voice. The rhythms are Scots, but different from Scots, more earthed and resonant. With much excusing and deprecation, a story begins: the storytelling is unobtrusively launched like a beached boat into a calm bay.

Gestures are restrained, but expressive, the face is mobile, the speaking fluent, multi-toned. We are drawn by quiet authority into the voice of the tale. There is no flashy invention here, no self-advertising ego, just the substance of the story, eloquently articulated, envisaged for our imagining.

All of nature is in this moment, with its seasonal rhythms, its bounties and cruel catastrophes. Ways of life measured by sea and land are in the undertow, generations are in the space of a breath and gesture.

Here be fairy folk, trolls, trows, mermaids, fishes, farmers, spirits and ghosts. But here also is love and sorrow, cherishing and loss, fulfilment and abandon. The swan maiden has flown, and the heart of the storyteller is wrung, vulnerable to our acceptance or rejection as listeners. How can we resist his gently self-disparaging wooing? We pledge ourselves to the story.

Tom Muir is a storyteller of the Northlands and Sagalands, not just of his native Orkney. In a cold world he keeps the flame of imagination aglow.

Here, he presents with simplicity and assurance some of the great northern tales. But listen for the voice, hunt down the opportunity to hear and meet the quiet, genial man who can open the gates of wonder.

Donald Smith, Director
The Scottish Storytelling Centre

Published by The Orcadian Limited (Kirkwall Press)

Hell's Half Acre, Hatston, Kirkwall, Orkney, KW15 1GJ

Tel. 01856 879000 • Fax 01856 879001 • www.orcadian.co.uk

Booksales: www.orcadian.co.uk/shop/index.php

Text: Tom Muir © 2015

Illustrations: Anna Anglemark © 2015

Story-telling recorded by Magnetic North Films, Evie, Orkney

ISBN 978-1902957-74-6

Printed in Orkney by The Orcadian, Hatston Print Centre,
Hell's Half Acre, Kirkwall, Orkney, Scotland, KW15 1GJ

contents

Introduction iii

Foreword v

Contents vii

The Legend of Storholmen 1

Assipattle and the Stoor Worm 7

Mallie and the Trow 13

The Swan Maiden 17

The Changeling in the Cradle 21

The Blacksmith and the Devil 25

Then the Merman Laughed 31

The Red and White Roses 33

Toller and the Good Neighbours 37

The Elf Maiden 43

How Tam Scott Lost His Sight 47

The Trolls and the Bear 51

East of the Sun and West of the Moon 55

The Two Sisters 63

The Witch's Horse 67

The Fiddler and the Trows' Foy 69

The Miser's Ghost 75

The Widow's son and the Fairy Princess 79

The City Under the Sea 85

Sheepskin Boy 93

The Author 98

the Legend of storholmen

This is the only modern story in this book, yet it has a feeling as old as the tree I sat under when the story came to me. I was invited to Storholmen, in the summer of 2007, by Mats and Britta Geschwind to tell traditional folk tales for the visitors to the Viking Village. Britta had said that there were no stories relating to Storholmen, and I had joked that there would be by the time I had left. Here, I had the great good fortune of meeting Anna Anglemark, the illustrator of this book, who took me to see the beauty of Oak Hill, which is a very different landscape from my native treeless Orkney. There, she showed me the three great oak trees that stand guard over the woods. One morning she told me that she needed to make a new bag of runic tablets to use in the village for fortune telling, but she needed them for that evening. I offered to help by sanding smooth the small wooden tablets, cut from the branch of a juniper tree, but this had to be done in secret as it was to be a surprise. Not feeling like sitting in my tent in darkness sanding the tablets, I took them to the three great oak trees that Anna had shown me. As I sat sanding these tablets smooth and ready for the runes to be seared into them, I emptied my mind of all thoughts and just enjoyed the sunshine and the beautiful view of the lake through the trees. It was then that this story started to form inside my head – just the idea at first, and then more detailed parts followed, not in order, but more like random memories. I took these fragments and wove them together until The Legend of Storholmen was formed. I had not set out to think of a story; it just came to me like a whispered secret. I told it to the assembled crowd by the open fire the following night and it seemed to move them. I now offer it to you; a story told to me by a tree.

Long, long ago, when the world was still young and the moon was but a child, there lived a great chief in the Northlands. He was a powerful and brave man; it was said of him that, when he was only fourteen years old, he killed a huge bear with his bare hands. He cut the largest claw from its mighty paws and he wore it around his neck, so the people called him 'Bear Claw'. This mighty warrior lived in the part of Sweden that we now call Storholmen, but in those days it looked very different. There was no lake there, only a deep valley that formed a clearing in the woods where a million brightly coloured flowers bejewelled the grass, like stars in a green sky. The deer used to graze in this clearing, and it was here that Chief Bear Claw liked to go hunting.

The forest that surrounded the clearing was the home of the light elves, whose king had a fine palace hidden deep within its borders. The King of the Elves had four daughters, all beautiful to behold, but the youngest was the fairest of them all. Every morning she left her father's palace and went to the clearing to sing to the morning sun as it rose above the

1

trees. Her voice was like silvery water running over polished stones, and it captivated every living thing that heard it. She sang her song of welcome to the dawn, a song of rejoicing for the great fiery ball that gives us light, warmth and life itself. Every morning the sun rose in the sky, and every morning she sang her song of welcome.

One morning, as she sang, Chief Bear Claw heard the beautiful sound floating on the breeze while he was hunting. He turned his horse and rode towards the sound, held captivated, like a man in a trance. Then he saw her, and her beauty captured his heart and soul like no other person or thing had ever done, and he knew then that he must make her his bride. When she saw him, she turned and fled back towards the forest, but he called to her to stop and not be afraid. She turned, her heart pounding in her breast as she looked towards the mortal man who had called so softly and tenderly to her. He walked over to her and looked into her sapphire blue

eyes. There was fear in her eyes, but there was also love when she looked at him, while the love in his eyes shone as brightly as the rising sun. They talked for a long time, and he held her close to his beating heart as the sun rose higher in the sky. After a while she had to leave, as her father would miss her and come looking for her if she didn't return to his palace among the trees. They agreed to meet again the following morning, and then they tore themselves from their loving embrace.

When she returned, her older sisters could see that something had happened to her, and she told them of the handsome stranger.

'A mortal man; father will never allow you to see a mortal man. He would kill the both of you before agreeing to that,' they warned her, but love now ruled her thoughts, not reason or logic.

Her sisters reluctantly agreed to keep her secret, and to weave stories to protect her from her father's wrath. Every morning she would

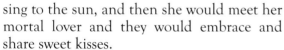

sing to the sun, and then she would meet her mortal lover and they would embrace and share sweet kisses.

When her father said:

'Where is my youngest daughter today? Why does she stay so long in the clearing?,' her sisters would say:

'Oh, father, she is gathering wild flowers to decorate the halls', or 'Why, she is searching for mushrooms for us to eat with our evening meal.'

He believed them, as he knew that she loved to be surrounded by things of beauty, and they all loved the mushrooms that grew deep in the forest.

One morning the king grew suspicious of the length of time that his daughter spent singing her song of welcome to the sun, and he decided to follow her. He saw her slip out of the forest and go down into the clearing before the sun rose. He saw her sing her song of joy

to greet the rising sun. He saw the mortal man who took her in his arms and kissed her lips. The rage grew inside his breast, hotter than a volcano, and more powerful than the ocean. Instead of taking his anger out on them, he returned home and hid his wrath under a smile. When his youngest daughter arrived home he said to her;

'Daughter, is there anything that you wish to tell me?'

'No, father' she replied, 'only that I love you.'

This answer did not satisfy him, and he brooded on what should be the fate of his youngest child and her mortal lover.

The next day the king waited until his daughter left the palace, and then he went to the stable to put the golden harness on his snow-white steed. The king's three older daughters saw him, and they ran to the clearing to warn their younger sister of the danger. They ran as fast as they could, but suddenly their father appeared over the hill on his horse, his eyes

flashing with rage. He saw his three oldest daughters running to warn their sister, and he knew that they had been lying all along in order to protect her. He raised his hand and cast a spell on them, turning them into three great oak trees. He then rode to the edge of the forest, where he could see his youngest daughter standing, ready to sing to the sun. He raised his hands in the air, and turned them around so that they cut a great double circle in the still morning mist. The young princess found herself lifted up into the air, turning around, spinning wildly as she felt her body change and grow. Her bones turned to cold, hard stone, while her flesh became earth and her long hair stiffened and turned into trees. There she stood, a girl no more, but a hill covered with trees that reached up to the sky.

The King of the Elves waited for her mortal lover to appear, so that he could suffer his fate as well. He saw him arrive - a fine, strong, handsome man he looked in the soft light of the morning sun. Chief Bear Claw looked around for the girl, but she was not there. He stared at the strange new hill that stood in the clearing, and his heart broke. He knew that something bad had happened, and he knew that he would never see his love again, so he sat down under the hill and he wept. The tears flowed down his face like a waterfall as he wept for his lost love. The King of the Elves was moved by the man's suffering and he felt pity for him. He had obviously loved his daughter very much, and, as his temper cooled, he felt a deep remorse for what he had done. He had transformed his daughters, but was now unable to undo the terrible spells that he had cast while his anger raged inside of him like a wild beast. No more would he see his beautiful girls as they danced and played in the woods; no more would he hear their laughter ringing through his halls, nor their voices joined together in song. He felt pity for the mortal man who sat and wept beneath the hill that had once been his love and his joy in

4

life, and he raised his hands one more time. His fingers danced, and, as they did so, the tears that the man shed turned into a great flood that filled the whole valley, and his body dissolved into water also. He was transformed into Lake Erken, which sparkles and glitters with the colour of the flowers that once graced the clearing, and the hill was now no longer a hill, but the island of Lillholmen. There it lies to this day, caressed by the tender embrace of its lover until the end of time. It is said that if you have love in your heart, you can hear the rippling waves sigh:

'I love you... love you... love you' as they kiss the shore.

The king also pitied his three eldest daughters who he had turned into oak trees, so he gave the eldest daughter special powers. Since it was talking that had condemned them to their fate, he gave the eldest daughter the power to communicate with people who seek wisdom, but only if they have good hearts. They can gain knowledge by sitting beneath that middle oak tree and listening with their heart, not their ears.

assipattle and the stoor worm

This story must have been taken to Orkney by the Vikings when they arrived in their longships. The great sea monster in this tale is a close relation to Jormondgand, the Midgarth Serpent that the Vikings believed was wrapped right around the world, biting on his own tail. That monster would be killed by the god Thor, who would himself die as a result of the fight, during the great battle of Ragnorok at the end of time, when the gods would be destroyed and a new world created.

There was once, a long, long time ago, a farmer who lived in a fine farm called Leegarth. It lay in a lovely green valley surrounded by hills, and a crystal clear stream danced for joy as it ran past the house. The farmer was not a wealthy man, and he and his wife and seven sons worked hard to put bread on the table. Well, that's not strictly true; you see the man and his wife and the six oldest sons worked hard, but the youngest son did nothing but lie by the side of the fire raking through the ashes. His clothes were covered with ashes, and when he did venture outside the ash blew from him like smoke from a bonfire. His family called him Assipattle, the ash raker, and his mother and father would look on him with sad eyes and shake their heads, but his older brothers hated him for his laziness, and they would kick him as they went out the door to their work. But Assipattle didn't mind, because he was a dreamer and he had the heart of a poet. He told great stories in which he was the hero who killed dragons and carried off fair maidens, but this only made his brothers hate him even more.

One day, a terrible thing happened – the Stoor Worm arrived at the coast of the land where Assipattle lived. This was the most evil of all the monsters that plagued mankind: a huge sea serpent that was so big that he had curled himself right around the world. Whenever he moved he caused tidal waves and earthquakes, and his foul breath was poisonous, killing every living thing that it touched. He could sweep whole towns into his great mouth with his huge forked tongue, and eat all the people who were in them just as easily as it is for us to blink an eye. What was worse, the Stoor Worm had started to yawn, which did not mean that he was tired: it meant that he was hungry and needed to be fed.

The king who lived in the great castle on top of the hill gathered together all his wisest advisers to try to find out what could be done to save the kingdom from destruction. Not one of them had any idea as to what could be done, but one of them suggested that they seek the advice of the old wizard who lived on the slopes of the mountain. The king sent his heralds to fetch the old wizard, who eventually arrived to offer the king his help. He was a very old man, yet he was still tall for his years. He wore a long robe of powder blue cloth and in his hand he held a staff. His long hair was as white as a snowdrift, and his beard hung down to his knees. The king asked him what should be done to save his kingdom from the destruction of the Stoor Worm, and the wizard thought for a long time, stroking his great white whiskers as he pondered the situation. He then spoke in a deep, clear voice.

'Your Majesty, the Stoor Worm has grown old, and he has in his time been all around the world, eating all sorts of exotic people, but now in his old age he has developed a . . . sweet tooth. I believe that if you were to feed him seven young maidens for his breakfast every Saturday morning then the Stoor Worm would spare your kingdom.' It was agreed that this should be done, and every Saturday morning seven young maidens were bound hand and foot and placed on a flat rock in front of the Stoor Worm's head. When the first rays of the morning sun touched the Stoor Worm's eyes it yawned seven great yawns, then it thrust out its long tongue and ate the first thing it touched. It picked up the seven maidens, one by one, between the forks of its tongue and popped them in its mouth like juicy sweet berries.

One Saturday morning, Assipattle and his family went to see the Stoor Worm eat his terrible breakfast. The old man went grey with horror as he watched the kingdom's finest girls being eaten.

'There will soon be no more girls left in the kingdom,' he wailed, 'and who will be left to marry my sons? If they don't find wives and have children, then who will look after us in our old age?'

'Don't worry, father,' said Assipattle, 'I will fight and kill the Stoor Worm.'

His brothers laughed when they heard this, and they drove him away by throwing stones and earth at him.

Later that evening, Assipattle's mother sent him to the barn to tell his brothers that their supper was ready. They were threshing corn on the barn floor when Assipattle appeared, and they set on him and held him down while they piled straw on top of him. They sat on his head, and would have smothered him if their father had not caught them in the act and stopped them. He was annoyed, and as they ate their supper he was still scolding his sons for their behaviour. Assipattle, still with straw in his hair, calmly said:

'Oh, it's alright, father, I would have given them a good thrashing if you had not stopped them when you did.' His brothers laughed, and the oldest one said:

'Then why didn't you then?'

'Oh, I'm saving my strength,' said Assipattle.

'Saving your strength?' said his oldest brother, 'What are you saving your strength for?'

'For when I fight the Stoor Worm,' said Assipattle.

'Boy,' said his father gravely, 'you'll fight the Stoor Worm when I make spoons from the horns of the moon.'

Time passed, and the people grew angry at the loss of their daughters. The king once more called on the wizard to attend the court in order to find a solution to the problem of the Stoor Worm once and for all.

The wizard grew pale when he heard this, and he said, 'Well, your Majesty, there is one way of ridding the land of the Stoor Worm, but it is too great a price to pay.'

'We have no option, wizard,' shouted the king. 'What is this price that we have to pay to be rid of this monster for all time?'

'Well,' stuttered the wizard, 'as you insist, it is this. You must give the Stoor Worm the loveliest maiden in the entire kingdom. You must feed the Stoor Worm your daughter, the princess Gem-de-lovely.'

A gasp rose from the king's councillors, then their voices burst forth with angry words of protest. How could he even say such a thing? The princess was the king's only child and, with her, the whole race of the old kings would die out forever. No, this could never be done!

'Silence!' shouted the king, 'It is a hard thing that you ask me to do wizard, but it is fitting, in a way. My daughter is indeed the last of the race of kings who are descended from the great god Odin himself, but it is fitting that my daughter should die so that her people can live.'

The king slumped back down on his throne, then he looked up and said, 'But yet, I will crave one last indulgence. Send a proclamation throughout the kingdom saying that if any brave knight can fight and kill the Stoor Worm, then he can have as his reward my magic sword, Sikkersnapper, which was a gift to my ancestors from the god Odin. My kingdom shall also be his, and my daughter's hand in marriage.'

The proclamation went throughout the kingdom like wildfire, and thirty-six brave knights rode into town to fight the Stoor Worm. The first twelve took one look at the Stoor Worm and rode straight through the town and out the other side and ran away home. The second twelve fainted with fright at the sight of the monster, and had to be carried home on stretchers. The third twelve just skulked around the king's castle until they found his wine cellar, then drowned their sorrows in the king's finest wine. The old king looked at them with disgust, as the blood of an older and nobler race ran through his veins. He ordered his men to prepare a boat and to bring him his magic sword, Sikkersnapper; he would fight the Stoor Worm himself. The news spread throughout the kingdom that the king was to fight the Stoor Worm the next morning at dawn. It even reached Leegarth, where Assipattle was still lying by the fire, raking among the ashes as usual. His parents were in bed talking, and he listened to their conversation with interest.

'So, the king's going to fight the Stoor Worm at dawn,' said his father. 'We should go to see that. We can take my horse, Teetgong; he's the fastest horse in the land, you know.'

'Yes,' snorted his wife, 'I know that.'

The old man was not always the most sensitive of men, but he knew that something was annoying his wife, and he summoned up his courage to ask her what it was.

'Is there something bothering you, my sweet?'

'Yes, there is!' she replied.

'Well, my dear,' said the old man, his voice trembling, 'what is it?'

'You are keeping secrets from me, that's what the trouble is!' said the old woman scornfully.

'Oh . . . well . . . why . . . I mean . . . no, I'm not,' said the old man. 'What secrets do I have from you?'

The old woman said, 'Your horse, Teetgong.'

'Fastest horse in the land' said the old man proudly.

'Yes,' said the old woman, 'but what I want to know is what makes it run so fast.'

'Oh, but dear, you don't need to know that.'

'Why?' snorted the old woman.

'Well, because it's, you know . . . a secret.'

'I thought as much,' snorted the old woman, 'and if you've got one secret from me, then you may have others!'

'Oh, I have no secrets,' protested the old man, 'you're making a fuss out of nothing'.

They argued for a while before the old man finally gave up and told his wife the secret.

'When I want Teetgong to stand as still as a statue, I give it a pat on the left shoulder. When I want him to run fast, I give him a pat on the right shoulder, but if I want him to run as fast as the wind, I blow through a goose's thrapple (windpipe). When he hears that sound he's off like lightning; I keep a thrapple in my coat pocket in case of emergencies.'

Happy at last, the old couple were soon snoring.

Assipattle had been listening to all of this and, when he was sure that his parents were asleep, he crept over to his father's coat and took the goose's thrapple from the pocket and slipped outside. He headed for the stable and opened the door as quietly as he could. When the horse, Teetgong, saw him he knew that this was not his master, and he started to kick and to rear up, but Assipattle gave him a pat on the left shoulder and he stood as still as a statue. He climbed up on the horse's back and gave him a pat on the right shoulder and Teetgong set off with a loud neigh. The noise woke the old man and his sons, and they ran outside and took horses and followed Teetgong, shouting 'Stop! Thief!'

Assipattle's father had no idea it was his son who was the thief, and soon his horse was catching up with him. The old man shouted as loud as he could:

'Hi, Hi Ho! Teetgong Whoa!'

Teetgong stopped dead in his tracks, but Assipattle pulled the goose's thrapple from his pocket and blew through it. When Teetgong heard the sound it made, he pricked up his ears, neighed loudly and set off as fast as an arrow from a bow; it was all that Assipattle could do to breathe as the horse ran so fast. When the old man and his sons saw this, they stopped and turned their horses for home, as they knew there was no way they could catch up with Teetgong.

Assipattle rode through the night until he came to the top of the cliffs that sloped down to the sandy shore of a large bay. There, in the bay, was a huge black island, but this was no island at all, it was the Stoor Worm's head. Assipattle rode down to the bay and quietly slipped into an old cottage that stood close to the shore. In it was an old woman asleep in her bed with a great grey cat curled up at her feet. The fire had been rested for the night with damp peats, as it was considered bad luck to let your fire go out, and bad luck to lend fire to a neighbour in case the luck of the house should leave with it. (It was also before matches were invented!) The fire smouldered in the damp peats which had been cut from the hill and dried that summer. Assipattle took a small iron pot from beside the fire and picked up a glowing peat and put it into the pot, before slipping quietly outside and heading for the shore. There he saw the king's boat, ready for him to sail for battle with the Stoor Worm. There was a guard on board, and he was shuffling about and flapping his arms to keep warm.

'Hello,' shouted Assipattle to him, 'I was just going to build a small fire to boil some limpets for my breakfast. Would you like to come and warm yourself by my fire?'

'I had better not,' replied the guard, 'because if they find out I've left my post I'll be beaten'.

'You had better stay where you are then,' replied Assipattle, as he started to dig a shallow hole in which to light his fire.

Suddenly, he started to jump around wildly, shouting:

'Gold! Gold! I've found gold! Look how it shines, like the mid-day sun. Gold!'

As soon as the guard heard this he jumped from the boat, pushed Assipattle away and started to dig in the dirt like a dog. Assipattle picked up his pot with the peat in it and ran to the boat, casting off the rope and hoisting the sail. He looked around in time to see the king and his men arrive, and he saw them dancing with rage on the shore.

Assipattle sailed the boat close to the Stoor Worm's mouth just as the rays of the rising sun kissed the monster's eyes, and it started to wake up and yawned the first of its seven great yawns. Assipattle positioned the boat next to the great mouth, so that when it yawned again the boat was swept right into the monster's mouth and down its huge throat. Down, down, deeper and deeper into the Stoor Worm went Assipattle and his boat, right down deep inside the Stoor Worm. Now the inside of the Stoor Worm was like one great huge tunnel, but every now and then there were other smaller tunnels leading this way and that, and some water gurgled down this tunnel, and some down that one, until the water got shallower and shallower and the boat grounded. The inside of the Stoor Worm glowed with a green phosphorescent light, so Assipattle could see what he was doing. He picked up the pot with the burning peat in it, and he ran and he ran until he found what he was looking for: the Stoor Worm's liver! Now, you know how much oil there is in fish livers, so imagine how much oil there would be in the Stoor Worm's liver. Assipattle took out his knife and cut a hole in the liver, then he dropped the burning peat into the hole. He blew and he blew and he better blew, until he thought his head was going to burst, but eventually the oil in the liver caught fire and started to burn fiercely. Assipattle ran back to the boat as fast as his legs would carry him.

Now the king was having a bad day. Not only did he have to get up really early to fight the Stoor Worm and face certain death, but he arrived at the bay just in time to see some idiot steal his boat and sail off to be swallowed by the Stoor Worm. Things just couldn't get any worse, he thought, as he paced to-and-fro on the beach. Suddenly, one of his men said:

'Your Majesty, I've never seen the Stoor Worm do that before.'

'Do what?' asked the king angrily.

'Well,' said the man, 'he's sort of . . . smoking.'

'Smoking?' bellowed the king.

'Yes, see for yourself,' said the man.

Sure enough, when the king looked he saw that thick, black smoke was billowing out of the Stoor Worm's mouth and nose. The Stoor Worm was feeling very ill, in fact it felt very sick indeed, and it retched up all the water that was inside of it. A huge tidal wave of water flowed from the Stoor Worm's mouth, and there on top of it was Assipattle in the boat. The king and his men, the old woman and her cat from the cottage (who had gone out to see what all the noise was about), and all the horses ran up the hillside to safety as the wave crashed on the shore below. Assipattle and the boat were cast up high and dry among them, and they stood together to watch the death of the Stoor Worm.

As it died, the Stoor Worm thrust out its huge tongue into the sky, so high that it caught hold of the moon. They said that it would have pulled the moon from the sky, but the fork of the Stoor Worm's tongue slipped over the horn of the moon and it fell back to earth with a great crash. The tongue cut a huge hole in the face of the earth, and water flowed into this hole, which cut off the lands of Norway and Sweden from Denmark. There it remains to this day, only we now call it the Baltic Sea, and the two great bays at either end are the forks of the Stoor Worm's tongue. As it died, the Stoor Worm raised its huge head and, when it fell back to earth with a resounding crash, some of its teeth were knocked out and landed in the sea. These teeth remain there to this day, but now we call them the Orkney Islands. It raised its head again, and once more it fell back to earth, casting more of its teeth into the sea, creating the Shetland Islands. A third time the great head rose, and more teeth were cast into the sea, forming the Faroe Islands. Then the Stoor Worm curled itself up into a tight lump and died, and there it remains to this day, only now we call it Iceland. The hot water that boils out of the ground, and the fires that leap from the mountains there, are caused by the liver of the Stoor Worm, which is still burning.

The king was delighted, and he took Assipattle in his arms and he called him his son. He strapped the magic sword, Sikkersnapper, to Assipattle's side, and he said:

'My boy, my sword and my kingdom are yours, as is my daughter's hand in marriage, if she will have you.'

The Princess Gem-de-lovely stepped forward and looked into the eyes of this strange young man who had saved the world from the evil Stoor Worm, and love flowered in her heart. Assipattle also fell in love with the beautiful princess, and they were soon married, to the great joy of everyone. They lived in happiness and prosperity, and if they are not dead, then they are living yet.

Anna Anglemark

mallie and the trow

This story I heard from my great friend, Lawrence Tulloch, and it has become my favourite story. Lawrence, a fine storyteller from Yell in Shetland, learned many of his stories from his father, Thomas Tulloch, but this story is from George Peterson, a native of Papa Stoor. I owe them my thanks for letting me use it.

Mallie and her husband Robbie lived in a small croft in Shetland with their four young bairns. Robbie was a sailor, who would sign on ships for a few months in the summer but return home for the winter, bringing with him enough money to live on. They would buy enough barley flour to fill the meal girnal (a wooden chest used for storing flour) and a barrel of pickled herrings to see them through the cold winter months. But, one year, Robbie never returned to Mallie and the bairns, and it was feared that he had been lost in a shipwreck or through disease on board his ship. Nobody knew, but Robbie never returned home again. Mallie had four hungry bairns to feed, and no money coming in. She got bits of jobs here and there, making dresses and repairing clothes, but it was scarcely enough to put food on the table, and her bairns were crying with hunger. She could bear it no longer and, swallowing her pride, she took a staff in her hand and put a straw basket called a kishie on her back and set off with her four bairns to beg for food.

They went to an old woman who lived up the hill, and who was known to have plenty of food and drink for herself. Mallie knocked on the door, which the old woman opened and peered suspiciously outside.

'Who's there?' demanded the old woman.

'It's me, Mallie, and my four bairns. We are hungry; we have no food. Would you be kind enough to spare a mouthful of something for us, as without it I don't know what will happen to us?'

The old woman's face twisted into a look of horror, and she replied:

'I'm an old woman, and I have no food to spare for the likes of you!'

Then she slammed the door in Mallie's face.

As they walked back down the hill the oldest boy's blood boiled with rage.

'Did you see that, mother?' he shouted, 'Did you see what was in that old woman's cupboard? It was full of bread, cheese, butter, meat, puddings and all sorts of food, far more than she could ever eat, and yet she wouldn't give us so much as a crumb! How could she do that to us?'

'Well, son,' said Mallie calmly, 'that is just her way. Some people share and others do not. But remember this, son – we are better than that; for while we may have nothing, we will always share what we have.'

And they walked home sadly to their empty house.

The youngest bairns were crying with hunger, so Mallie tucked them up in their warm bed to sleep. At least sleep would make them forget their misery. Mallie made up the fire and returned to her sewing. Suddenly there was a knock at the door. 'It is late at night, so who could be calling at this hour?' wondered Mallie, as she opened the door. There stood a tiny man dressed in grey, and with a grey hat on his head. His whiskers bristled, and his dark eyes sparkled with mischief, and Mallie knew that this must be a hill trow, as the fairy folk are called in Shetland.

'I'm an old man in need of food and shelter,' said the trow, 'can I come in?'

'I'm sorry, old man,' said Mallie, 'but I'm afraid that you've picked the wrong house, for I have no food to give you. Maybe you could try another house?'

'I'm an old man,' said the trow, 'and I'm very tired from walking. I'll take my chances here.'

'Come in, come in,' said Mallie, 'and take a seat by the fire and warm yourself.'

She put more peats on the fire and made the trow comfortable.

The trow looked around the tiny house, and he saw the four bairns peering bleary-eyed at him from the foot of the bed.

'Come on, woman!' said the trow, 'you must have something to eat in the house.'

'Well, I'll try,' said Mallie.

She went over to the empty meal girnal and she took a knife and scraped the sides of it to remove any flour dust still sticking to it. She gathered together a small pile of flour, dust, cobwebs and wood shavings and she carefully gathered them up into a cup. She took this over to the empty barrel that had contained the brine that the herring had been pickled in, and she poured a small amount of the pickle onto the flour and dust and she mixed it into a paste before carefully dividing it into six equal parts: one for the trow, one each for her four children and one for herself. The trow stared at this disgusting substance, more like wallpaper paste than food, and he said:

'Is this all you have?'

'Yes,' said Mallie sadly, 'this is the only food in this house, and tomorrow we won't even have this much to eat.'

The trow scratched his head, and then he cheered up a bit, saying:

'Ah, but you'll have a fine drop of home-brewed ale to wash this stuff down with?'

'No, I'm sorry,' said Mallie, 'I have no barley for malt to make ale, but there is good sweet water from the well.'

'Ugh! No, thank you!' said the trow, 'I never touch the stuff.'

'I told you that you had picked the wrong house,' said Mallie, 'but at least you will be warm tonight, as I have plenty of peats to burn, so don't be cold.'

With that she retired to bed with the bairns, and left the trow sitting in the chair by the fire.

The next morning the trow said his goodbyes and headed for the door. He stopped and turned to Mallie and said;

'Was that truly all the food that you had in the house? That... stuff... you gave me, was that all that you had?'

'Truly it was,' said Mallie.

'Well then,' said the trow, 'it takes a very special kind of person to share the last food they have in the world with a total stranger. You have my blessings.'

And with that the trow left Mallie's house and disappeared from view.

'Well, my boy,' said Mallie to her oldest son, 'we may be starving, but we may as well be comfortable while we starve! Go and bring in some peats so that we can be warm.'

The boy brought in a kishie full of peats and set it by the fire. Mallie picked up a large peat and broke it in two so that it would burn easily, and as she did so she heard a 'ching' on the floor. She looked down, and there was a gold coin lying shining by her hearth. She broke another peat, and 'ching', another gold coin fell from it. She broke another, and another, and another peat, and every one had a gold coin inside of it. Mallie realised that this was the blessing that the trow had mentioned, and she gathered up all the money and said to her oldest son:

'Run into town, and buy bread, and cheese and butter; oh, and some ham and some tea. Oh, and strawberry jam — do remember jam Run!'

And away the boy ran to buy food. Mallie and her four bairns ate like royalty, and every peat that they broke had a gold coin in it.

Now word spread that Mallie had come into money. She had been as poor as a church mouse, but now she had plenty of money. The old woman who lived up the hill grew jealous.

'A beggar woman living like a queen. Who ever heard of such a thing?' she muttered to herself.

'I'll find out her secret. Why should she have all that money? Why shouldn't I, a poor old woman, share in this good fortune too?'

That night the old woman sneaked silently down the hill, and she spied on Mallie. As she peered through the window she saw Mallie break open a peat and a gold coin fall onto the floor.

'So that's her game, is it?' muttered the old woman, and she crept back up the hill to wait until they were asleep.

When she saw that the house was in darkness she crept back down the hill with a kishie on her back and she stole Mallie's peats. All night she carted peats from Mallie's peat stack back to her own house, where she piled them by the fire.

When dawn broke the old woman was ready to receive her reward. She took hold of a good big peat and she broke it in two, but, instead of it containing a gold coin, a live mouse fell to the floor and scuttled away into a corner.

'Hmm,' muttered the old woman, 'it must have been a dud. I'll try again.'

She broke another peat, and another live mouse fell to the floor, and then another mouse, and another mouse, until she had broken all of the peats that she had stolen from Mallie. She had not got one gold coin, but she did have a lot of mice. The mice gathered together in the corner and had a conference.

'Well,' said the head mouse, 'I don't know about you lot, but I'm hungry! What's to eat in this house?' And with that they ran to the old woman's cupboard that was full of food.

They ate her bread and her cheese, her butter and her meat and all the puddings. They nibbled holes in her clothes, her curtains, her furniture; they literally ate her out of house and home until she had nothing. The old woman was forced to take her staff in her hand and a kishie on her back (which had to be patched with dried grass, as the mice had nibbled holes in it), and she set off to Mallie's house to beg.

When the knock came to Mallie's door her oldest boy answered it. There stood the old woman, her clothes full of holes and a sheepish look on her face.

'Please pity a poor, hungry old woman,' she begged. 'My house has been overrun with mice, and they have eaten all my food and nibbled all my things. There is nothing left, and I'm hungry.' The boy stared at the old woman, and the rage he had felt before when she refused them food rose in his breast. He stared into her eyes and said in a cold voice:

'Old woman, I will give you exactly what you gave us when we were starving. Nothing!'

And with that he slammed the door in the old woman's face. Mallie had been watching this, and she stepped forward, shaking her head and saying:

'No, son. I told you, we are better than that. We share.'

Mallie opened the door and called to the old woman. 'Old woman, come back. Here, take as much food as you want, and remember this, as long as I'm living you will never have to go hungry.'

the swan maiden

This beautiful tale has the same theme as the stories from my native Orkney of the selkie folk. They swim in the sea as selkies (seals), but they have the power to remove their sealskins and dance on the shore twice a year on the night of the Spring Tide. When a young man steals a selkie woman's skin, then she has to follow him until she can get it back and return to the sea.

There was once a young hunter who lived with his foster-mother in a wooden house among the trees. He would go out every day on his horse to hunt the wild animals and birds that lived in the forest and by the sea. One Thursday evening at sunset he was down by the seashore, where the sand was golden and fine. He heard the sound of fluttering wings, and he hid himself in the bushes to see what birds were about to land on the water, and whether they were worth trying to catch for the pot. He saw three beautiful snow-white swans come gliding down, landing gracefully on the clear blue water with hardly a ripple. He gazed in wonder as these swans took off their mantles of feathers and laid them down on the soft green grass. There before him stood three beautiful women, with milk-white skin, and golden hair that played around their bodies like sunlight glittering on snow. The robes of feathers that they had taken off had turned into fine linen dresses as they lay on the grass, and the three maidens swam and played together in the water. One of the maidens, the youngest of the three sisters, was even more beautiful than the other two, and the young man watched her as she splashed in the water. Love for this swan maiden filled his heart, and he could think of nothing but how beautiful she was. After a while the three maidens left the water and went to where their garments of linen lay on the green grass, and they slipped them on and were once more swans. They spread their wings and flew away from sight, leaving the young hunter with the flame of love burning brightly in his heart.

When he returned home his foster-mother could tell that there was something wrong with him, but she left him in peace, thinking that he would be his usual self in a day or two. That night, the young man tossed and turned in his bed, as he passed a sleepless night thinking about the beautiful swan maiden that he loved so much. The next day he seemed even more sad and withdrawn, and he took no pleasure in hunting and no thrill in the chase. His foster-mother sat by his side that evening and asked him what the matter was.

'Oh, my dear mother,' he said with tears in his eye, 'I saw three swans alight on the sea yesterday, and they took off their feathers and became maidens. The youngest was so beautiful that I think I would rather die than live without her.'

'Oh, my poor boy,' said his foster-mother, 'I can see that you will never again have any joy in this world if you do not win this swan maiden for your wife. I can advise you on this matter, so listen closely to my words and maybe you will be happy in the end. Next Thursday, at sunset, go back to the shore where you first saw her, and she will return with her sisters to swim in human form. Watch carefully where she places her linen dress, the one that is really her feathers. Watch closely, my boy, and, when she goes to the water to swim, go and snatch it and hide it away somewhere that she won't find it. You will hear the sound of two swans flying away, but without her feathers she cannot return to the sky with her sisters.

She will come to you, and she will go down on her knees and she will beg you to return her feathers, but you must not do it! No matter how hard she begs, no matter how much she cries, you must keep hold of that dress of feathers, or she will be lost to you forever. As long as you have her feather dress, she will be in your power.'

The days passed slowly for the young man, and every hour seemed to last a day for him.

When, at last, Thursday came around again the hours seemed to last a week. The young man went down to the seashore before sunset, and hid himself in a bush and waited for the swans to arrive. As the setting sun painted the sky red and gold he heard the familiar sound of wings beating the air, and the three snow-white swans glided down to land on the sea. They cast off their feathers, which seemed to take the form of a linen dress, and they placed them on the grass before splashing into the sea to swim and play. The young man crept down to where the garments lay and stole the dress belonging to the youngest swan maiden, and he slipped away from the shore and hid it among the fallen leaves under a large bush. He waited out of sight of the maidens, who swam and played as they always did. After a while the swan maidens returned to their dresses, and when they put them on their feathers fluttered in the breeze and they spread their wings and flew away. The young man could hear the flutter of wings fading away into the distance, but he could also hear the sobs of the youngest swan maiden as she searched for her lost feathers. Suddenly, she stood before him, shaking with fear and sobbing. She dropped onto her knees and she begged him to have pity on her and to return her feather dress, but he hardened his heart and refused her pleas. Instead, he wrapped her up in his cloak and lifted her onto his horse and took her home to his house among the trees where his foster-mother was waiting.

The young man's foster-mother prepared a wedding for them, and soon he was married to the swan maiden. They lived together in happiness in the house among the trees, but the man kept the feather dress hidden from his bride. Their marriage was blessed with children, and it was said that there were no other children in the whole country that could match them for beauty or intelligence. So

19

things passed in this manner for seven years, and the man's happiness seemed complete.

One Thursday night, as the man and his swan wife were preparing for bed, he told her the story of how he had won her for his bride. He told her of how he had first seen her, and how he had fallen in love with her. He told her of his foster-mother's advice, and how he had stolen her dress of feathers.

'Do you still have that dress?' she asked.

'Why, yes, I do still have it,' he replied.

'May I see it?' she asked, smiling sweetly at her husband.

He took the dress from its hiding place and placed it on his wife's lap. She stood up and, before he knew what was happening, she had slipped on the dress of feathers and become a swan once more. She flew out of an open window and into the night. The man cried out, but it was too late; she had left him for ever. His heart broke, and he died not long after losing his swan wife, whom he loved more dearly than life itself.

the changeling in the cradle

This story is common throughout Scotland and the Northern Isles of Orkney and Shetland. It was once believed that the fairies (or trows in the Northern Isles) would steal newborn babies and replace them with a changeling. Women who were expecting a child would try to hide the fact in case the fairies found out, and a baby was never left unattended in case it was stolen. The fairies could not stand objects made of iron or steel, so a knife, or some such implement, was left in the bed with the mother and baby for protection. I have used a slightly different ending from a similar story here, because this is the way that I told it at Storholmen.

There was once a young couple who had a fine wee baby boy called Johnnie, and they loved him very much. One day the mother had to go out to get water from the well, and she left the baby unattended. When she returned the baby was not like his usual self; he was a scraggy wee thing, and he just lay there crying 'Nya, nya, nya' all day long. He never grew, never put on weight, but he ate like a horse and all the time he cried 'Nya, nya, nya!' The poor parents were worn thin by him and never got peace to sleep, but they remained devoted to the wee monster all the same.

One day there was to be a market in town and the couple wanted to go, but they needed someone to look after the baby. They went to the neighbouring house to ask the tailor who lived there if he would be good enough to look after the baby for the day, and he was a kindly man, so he agreed. He went to their house, and as he entered the constant whining of the baby filled the place. He looked at it as it lay there going 'Nya, nya, nya', but he just sat down by the fire and started to sew the trousers that he was making. The parents thanked him, and they left the house to go to the market.

No sooner were they out of the door when a gruff voice said:

'Is my mother and father away?'

The tailor looked around, but he could see nobody. He went to the window and looked out, but not a living soul was there. Thinking he must have been imagining things, he returned to his sewing.

'Is my mother and father away?' said the voice again.

This time the tailor looked towards the direction that the voice came from, and there, to his amazement, sat the baby, bolt upright in his cradle with his tiny wee hand clutching both sides of it.

'Eh, well, yes, they are away,' said the tailor.

'Good!' said the baby, 'I thought I'd never get rid of them.'

Then the baby pointed to a cupboard in the corner of the room, and he said to the tailor: 'There's a bottle of whisky in that cupboard; bring it down and we'll have a dram.'

The tailor found the bottle of whisky, and he poured two glasses of whisky, one for himself and one for the baby. The baby poured the

whisky down his throat in one quick gulp, smacked his lips approvingly, and then said:

'That was good, give us another one!'

The tailor poured out another dram for the both of them, then the baby started to get restless.

'What we need is some music!' said the baby, 'Go out to the barn and fetch me a corn straw.'

The tailor went to the barn and brought back a corn straw and handed it to the baby, who nipped it down to the size that he wanted, and then bored holes into it and started to play it like a tin whistle. The lively music cheered up the tailor, and he drank whisky and clapped his hands to the music that the baby played on the corn straw all that afternoon. As soon as the baby saw his parents pass by the window he threw the corn straw onto the fire and gestured towards the cupboard for the tailor to hide the bottle of whisky. As soon as they came in through the door he was lying back in the cradle again, going 'Nya, nya, nya.'

The tailor said quietly to the man:

'Would you come with me, I have some news for you.'

They went to the barn, and the tailor told the father what had happened that afternoon about the whisky and the whistle playing, but he didn't believe it.

'Well, that's easily settled,' said the tailor. 'Just say that there are still lots of things to sell and the market is carrying on tomorrow. Pretend to leave, but you watch and listen and you'll see what you'll see.'

The following day the tailor was sent for again, and the couple got dressed in their best clothes to go to the market. The baby watched them with cold eyes, but he kept up his crying all the time. Once they had gone he sat bolt upright in the cradle and said to the tailor:

'Is my mother and father away?'

Everything followed as it had done the day before; the whisky bottle was brought out and the corn straw was played, but this time

the disbelieving parents watched through the window in amazement. When they pretended to return home the baby threw away the straw and the bottle was replaced, and he started to cry, 'Nya, nya, nya.'

The parents slipped out to the barn with the tailor and said to him:

'What is that thing in the cradle, and what can we do about it?'

'That,' said the tailor, 'is a changeling. One of the fairy folk has taken your baby and replaced him with that creature, and by the sounds of him he's no baby!'

'But that's not possible; we never left him alone for a second,' said the man.

'Oh, my God,' said the woman. 'There was that one time I went to the well and left him alone.'

'Aha!' said the tailor, 'that must have been when they changed your baby. Listen to me, and you'll get your baby back. Tomorrow, pretend that you are going to brew ale, but use eggshells instead of a copper pot. If he gives himself away, throw him onto the fire and you'll get your baby back.'

The next day the woman was up early.

'Time to brew some ale for the harvest work,' she said, and she took two or three empty eggshells and filled them with water, then placed them carefully by the fireside to boil.

The baby was watching her, still going 'Nya, nya, nya,' but as this strange ritual was carried out he stopped his crying, and sat up in the cradle and stared at her like she was mad. Then, in a deep, gruff voice he said:

'I am old. I have seen the acorn before the oak, but I have never seen a brewery in an eggshell before!'

No sooner were the words out of his mouth than the father grabbed him and threw him on the fire. He disappeared up the chimney in a blue flame, and at that same moment there was a knock at the door and there outside lay their own baby, as healthy and happy as ever.

Anna Anglemark

the Blacksmith and the Devil

This story was collected by Peter Christen Asbjørnsen (1812–1885) and Jørgen Moe (1873–1882) in Norway in the first half of the 19th century. I had not heard this version of the story until I was given a book of short stories by my dear friend and fellow storyteller, Maritha Nielsen, while I was storytelling in Stavanger, Norway, in August 2007. She loved the story and wanted me to have it, and I felt that it was fated to be in this collection. I am familiar with versions of this story from Ireland and Scotland.

A long, long time ago, when Christ and St Peter walked among us, there lived a blacksmith. This blacksmith was greedy and ambitious, so he had sold his soul to the Devil in return for being the master of all the smiths. The Devil had smiled sweetly as he pointed to the spot where the blacksmith was to sign his name, and he added his own name underneath it to make the transaction binding. The blacksmith had agreed that the Devil could come and claim his soul after seven years, and so he became the greatest of all the smiths, and he had a sign made saying 'Here Lives the Master of all Masters', and he hung it above the door of his blacksmith shop.

One day Christ and St Peter were passing when they saw the sign, and, being curious, they went in to see who had made such a boast. There they saw the blacksmith at his anvil, and Christ said to him:

'Who are you?'

'Read the sign over the door,' said the blacksmith, 'or if you can't read, then sit there and wait for somebody who can.'

Christ was not amused by this reply, but before he could open his mouth a man arrived leading a horse that needed its shoes repairing.

Christ said:

'I can shoe your horse for you.'

'Alright,' said the blacksmith, 'because no matter how bad a job you make of it, I will be able to put it right.'

Christ went over to the horse with a saw and he cut off one of its front legs and carried it over to the forge. He pumped the bellows until the coals were hot, and then put the horse's hoof into the fire until the shoe was red hot, and then he beat it and sharpened the nails until it shone like new, then he just put the leg back on the horse as good as new. He cut off the other front leg and did the same thing with it. Then he did the back legs, one at a time, just like the front ones, and the horse trotted out of the smithy as if nothing had happened.

The blacksmith was impressed at this trick, and he said to Christ:

'You are not a bad blacksmith after all.'

'Oh,' said Christ 'is that right?'

Just then the blacksmith's old mother hobbled down to the smithy to tell him that his dinner was ready. She was very old and bent almost double with age, and her brown face was a mask of wrinkles. Christ turned to the blacksmith and said:

'Watch this carefully, and you'll see what you'll see.'

And with that he grabbed the old woman and dumped her on the forge, covering her with coals and pumping the bellows until the heat of the forge was almost unbearable. The blacksmith was horrified, but, to his amazement, Christ drew out his old mother from the flames, but she was not an old woman any more. The wrinkles had gone from her apple blossom cheeks and her grey hair had turned to gold, and she was transformed into a young girl. She giggled and ran away, skipping happily. The blacksmith looked at Christ and said:

'Like I said before, you are quite a blacksmith. The sign above my door says I am the master of all the masters, but I see it's true that you live and learn.'

He left them in the smithy and went home to have his dinner, and to drag away his recently ancient mother who was now busy flirting with a young ploughman.

When the blacksmith returned after his meal he found the two strangers were still in his smithy. A man came in leading a horse that needed new shoes, and the blacksmith thought that it was his turn to show what he was capable of.

'Bring the horse over here,' he ordered, 'I've learned a new way of working that will save time when the days are short.'

He took a saw and he cut off all four of the horse's legs, saying to Christ:

'It's faster doing them all together.' He piled coals on the fire and put the legs in the forge, as he had seen Christ do, and he ordered his apprentice to pump the bellows. The horse's legs were burnt to ashes, and the blacksmith had to pay the man for the loss of his horse.

Now the blacksmith was not too impressed

with this, and he was determined to demonstrate to this upstart stranger who the best smith was. He saw an old woman pass by, and he grabbed her and set her on the forge and piled coals over, and got the apprentice to pump the bellows for all he was worth. The old woman screamed and prayed for mercy, but the blacksmith just said:

'Hold your tongue, old woman! I'm doing you a great favour, and I won't even charge you for it.'

The poor old woman was burnt to a cinder, just like the horse's legs had been.

'That's a shame,' said Christ.

'Oh, she'll never be missed' said the blacksmith, 'but the real shame is on the Devil, because he is not keeping the promise that hangs above my door.'

Christ now understood the reason why he had made such a claim on the sign above the door: he had sold himself to the Devil. Thinking that maybe the poor sinner deserved another go, he said to him:

'What if I could grant you three wishes? What would you wish for?'

'Why don't you try me,' said the blacksmith, sensing that the stranger was not all that he seemed to be.

'Alright,' said Christ, 'what are your three wishes?'

'Well,' said the blacksmith, 'my first wish would be that, if I tell someone to climb up the pear tree outside of my smithy, then they will be stuck there until I granted them permission to climb down. My next wish is that, if I ask someone to sit in the armchair in my workshop, they will be stuck there until I tell them that they can get up. My last wish is that whatever goes into my steel mesh purse has to remain inside until I decide that it can come out.'

Christ was furious:

'You fool!' he bellowed, 'you have wasted your wishes! Your first wish should have been to seek the grace and goodwill of God.'

'Oh, no!' said the blacksmith, 'I couldn't ask for such a great honour as that.'

Christ and St Peter bade the blacksmith a good-day, and then they stomped off in a rage.

Now time went by as fast in those days as it does now, and the seven years passed by in a flash. The day arrived when the Devil called on the blacksmith in order to collect his soul. The blacksmith smiled at him, saying: 'Good morning, you old Devil."

'Not so much of the "old", thank you,' replied the Devil. 'Right, blacksmith; are you ready to come with me to hell?'

'Well, yes, in a minute,' said the blacksmith. 'You see, I hate to leave a job unfinished, and I have a head to put on this nail, so I'd like to do that before I go. But you must be hungry and thirsty after your journey; why don't you climb up that pear tree and eat some of those nice juicy pears?'

'Well,' said the Devil, 'I don't mind if I do.'

The Devil climbed up the pear tree and started to eat the fruit. After a while the blacksmith came out and said:

'I'm having a bit of trouble with this nail. You see, the iron is as hard as the very devil... oh, I'm sorry, no offence meant.'

'No offence taken,' said the Devil, as he lazily munched on a juicy pear.

'Yes, it will take a bit longer to finish this job.'

The Devil frowned and said:

'How much longer?'

'Oh, about four years, I would say', said the blacksmith.

The Devil grew red with rage and tried to climb down from the tree, but he was stuck fast. He swore and cursed at the blacksmith, but he eventually had to calm down and listen to him.

'You can't come down from that tree unless I command it, so you are stuck there for four years.'

'Please let me down... old friend,' said the Devil, so he agreed to leave the blacksmith alone for another four years.

When the years had passed the Devil returned to collect the blacksmith and to take him to hell.

'Good day,' said the Devil, 'I presume that you've managed to put a head on that nail by this time?'

'Why, yes,' said the blacksmith, 'but you have arrived a bit too soon, because I still have to sharpen it. Sit down there in that armchair and make yourself comfortable.'

The Devil sat down, and started to think of all the horrible things that he was going to do to the blacksmith as soon as he got him back to hell.

'I'm having a few problems with sharpening this nail,' said the blacksmith, 'I think I'll need another four years yet.'

'No!' shouted the devil, 'no more time; you're coming with me this very minute.'

But the Devil couldn't get up out of the armchair. He was stuck fast. He roared and he cursed, but no matter how hard he tried he couldn't get out of that chair. He then pleaded with the blacksmith to release him and, after he agreed to leave him alone for another four years, he was allowed to leave the armchair and go back to hell.

Four more years passed, and the Devil once more returned to collect the blacksmith's soul.

'Are you ready this time?' asked the Devil.

'Yes, I'm ready to go,' said the blacksmith cheerily, fastening his coat ready for the journey.

As he chatted happily to the Devil the blacksmith said:

'There is one thing I've been meaning to ask you.'

'What's that, then?' asked the Devil.

'Well, people say that you are a very powerful man, and that you can do anything you want.'

'Why, yes,' said the Devil, puffing out his chest with pride, 'that I can.'

'I've even heard,' said the blacksmith, 'that you can change size as you wish. Surely that can't be true?'

'Oh, it's true alright,' said the Devil.

'You know,' said the blacksmith, 'I'd like to see that. You see this old steel mesh purse I have here? I think there may be a hole in it, and I don't want to lose my travel money, so could you make yourself so small that you can slip inside of it?'

'No problem,' said the Devil, and as quick as a flash he shrank down to the size of a fly and slipped into the purse.

The blacksmith snapped the purse shut with the Devil inside of it.

'There are no holes in your purse,' said the Devil, 'so let me out.'

'Oh, I know that,' said the blacksmith, 'but it's better to be safe than sorry.'

He threw coals onto the forge fire and pumped the bellows until it burned brightly, and then he threw the steel mesh purse containing the Devil into the hottest part of the fire.

'Ooh! Ow! What are you doing?' said the Devil, 'I'm still in here, you know!'

When the blacksmith had heated the purse until it glowed almost white hot, he took it from the forge and put it on the anvil, saying: 'I'd better make sure that the seams are soldered well enough,' and he started to beat on the purse with all his might.

'Ooh! Ow! Ouch! Stop it! Stop it!' squealed the Devil, 'Let me go and I promise never to come after you again.'

So the blacksmith plunged the hot purse into the bucket of water and let the Devil free. He ran away to hell without a backward glance and he never troubled the blacksmith again.

Now the time passed, the blacksmith started to think that he had maybe been a bit too hasty in beating the Devil, because if he was refused admission into heaven then it would not be good to be on such bad terms with the ruler of hell, and he might find himself without a place to stay. He decided to find out, and slinging his hammer over his shoulder he set off on the journey to hell. After walking for a long time he came to the crossroads that branch off to heaven and hell. He met a tailor, who was shuffling along the road slowly with his pressing iron in his hand.

'Where are you off to?' enquired the blacksmith.

'I'm going to heaven,' said the tailor.

'Well, I can't keep you company for long, because I'm off to hell', said the blacksmith, and with large strides he marched off towards hell at a brisk pace.

When the blacksmith arrived at the gates of hell he knocked on the door as loudly as he could. A watchman slid open the shutter of a small peep-hole and looked out at him.

'What do you want?' asked the watchman.

'Go and tell the Devil that there is someone to see him,' replied the blacksmith, and so the watchman slammed shut the shutter of the peep-hole and went off to see the boss.

'There's a man outside who wants to see you,' the watchman told the Devil.

'Go and ask who it is,' ordered the Devil, so the watchman returned to the blacksmith to ask him who he was.

'Tell the Devil that it's the blacksmith who owned the purse. Tell him I'm tired, as I worked until noon and then walked for the rest of the day, so I want to come in and rest.'

When the Devil heard this he turned white with fear, and shouted:

'Don't let him in! Lock the gates of hell. Lock all nine locks, and put another bar on the gates as well. If that man gets in here he will create havoc, and I've just got the place looking nice, too!'

So they rushed to the gates and locked them securely. When the blacksmith heard all the commotion, and the sound of the keys turning in the locks, he knew that he was not welcome in there, so he turned around and went back up the road as fast as he could.

The blacksmith now thought he had no option but to try his luck with heaven, so he walked at a brisk pace back to the crossroads where he had left the tailor, and took the road leading to heaven. As he neared the gates of heaven he saw that they were open a little bit in order to let the poor, thin-looking tailor squeeze through. When St Peter saw the blacksmith heading towards the gates he tried to shut them as fast as he could. The blacksmith took his hammer and threw it at the gap in order to prevent the gates from closing on him. If the blacksmith didn't get through that gap in the gates of heaven, then I don't know what has become of him.

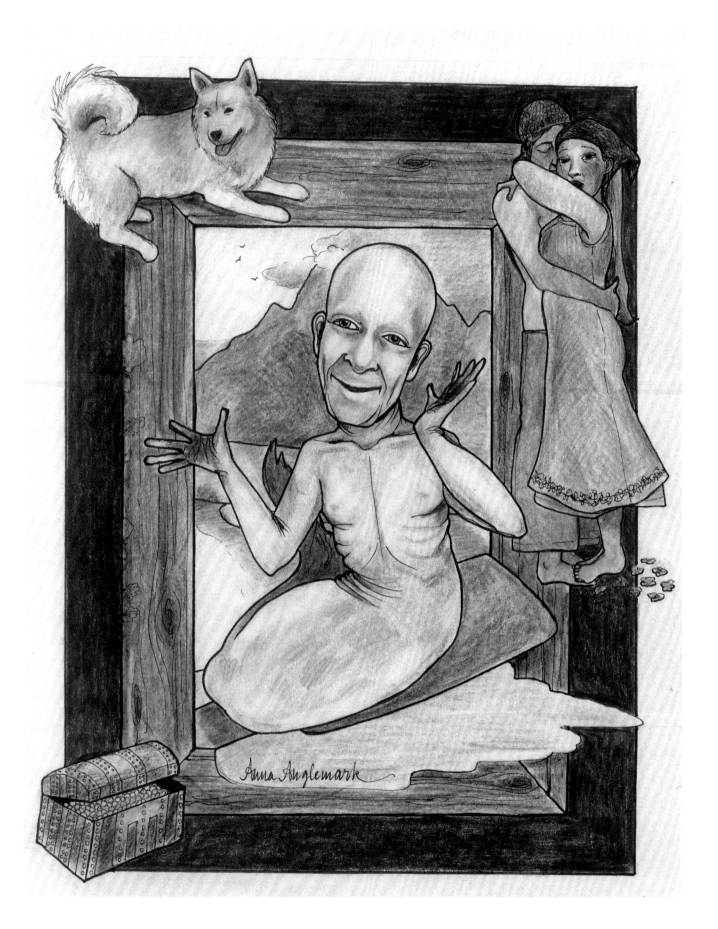

Anna Anglemark

then the merman Laughed

The title of this story has become a proverb in Iceland. I have read another version of this story from Iceland, but this is the version I have heard from my friend Hjorleifur Helgi Stefansson, a very fine storyteller from Iceland, who learned his stories from his grandparents. His version is the finest, so it is the one that I will share with you. My thanks go to him for allowing me to use this story.

There was once a fisherman in Iceland who went out in his boat to fish. He was having some luck, pulling in this kind of fish and that kind of fish on his baited hooks. Then, below him in the water, he saw a dark shape moving. He thought it might be a shark, and he knew that he could get big money for one of those, so he took out his largest hook and tried to catch it. The shape drifted in and out of his view until he felt the line tighten, and he pulled as hard as he could to land this valuable catch. He pulled and pulled until the creature broke the surface of the water; but this was no shark, but a merman. He pulled the merman into his boat and he sat and stared at the strange-looking creature. He was a small man with a large head and round flat hands, and the lower half of him looked like a seal. He was grey in colour, naked and with not a hair on his body. The merman spoke to the fisherman, saying:

'Put me back in the sea at once. I was on my mother's roof fixing it for her when you caught me, and she will worry when I don't come home. Let me go.'

'No, I will not,' said the fisherman, 'you are coming home with me.'

The fisherman knew that the merman had the power to see things that are hidden to mortal men, and he knew that it would prove lucky in the long term.

The fisherman rowed his boat back to the shore and pulled it safely up the beach and secured it. He gathered his gear together, and he picked up the merman and carried him back to his house. On his way home he caught his foot on a small tussock of grass that grew on a small mound and he stumbled and nearly fell. The fisherman was angry, and he swore at the tussock, and cursed the fact that it had been sent to his farm to be a nuisance to him. Then the merman laughed; 'Hah, hah, hah!'

'What are you laughing at?' asked the fisherman, but the merman said nothing.

As the fisherman neared his house, his dog came running to greet him with its tail wagging wildly. The dog jumped up at his master, but the fisherman shouted at him:

'Clear off, dog!' and gave it a kick.

Then the merman laughed, 'Hah, hah, hah!'

'What is it?' demanded the fisherman, 'What are you laughing at this time?' But the merman said nothing.

When the fisherman reached his house he was greeted by his wife, who threw her arms around his neck and kissed him. She was a young woman, very pretty, and he loved her very dearly.

'Oh, I'm so glad to see you, darling,' she said, kissing him again.

Then the merman laughed,'Hah, hah, hah!'

'What is it now?' asked the fisherman, 'Why are you laughing at me? You had better watch yourself, merman, because I've just about had enough of you.'

But the merman remained silent.

Later that night the fisherman sat staring at the merman, who refused to speak to him. He knew that the merman had knowledge way beyond anything that he had, and that maybe he could tell him something of value. After a while the fisherman asked the merman:

'Why did you laugh at me today? You laughed at me three times. What for?'

'Stupidity,' answered the merman.

'What do you mean?' asked the fisherman.

'Take me back home to my mother and I'll tell you,' replied the merman. 'Return me to the very spot where you caught me and I'll tell you why I laughed.'

The fisherman agreed, and the next day he carried the merman back down to his boat.

The fisherman rowed out to sea to the very same spot where he had caught the merman, and he lifted him onto the blade of his oar and held him out over the surface of the water.

'Well,' he said, 'now are you going to tell me why you laughed at me?'

'Yes,' said the merman, 'I'll tell you. When you were walking home you tripped on a tussock and you cursed it. Then I laughed, because under that tussock is buried a great treasure that is intended for you. Only for you. Then your dog ran out to greet you and you kicked it, and I laughed again, because that dog truly loves you. He is devoted to you and he would sacrifice his own life to protect you, and yet you treat him like dirt. The third time I laughed was when your young wife hugged you and you kissed her lovingly. She doesn't love you; in fact, she hates you and wishes that you were dead. She is having an affair with the postman right under your nose, but you are too blinded by your desires to see it.'

'That's a lie!' shouted the fisherman.

'No, it's not!' replied the merman firmly.

He then jumped from the oar blade into the sea with a splash and was gone.

The fisherman sailed home right away with the merman's words ringing in his head like church bells. He went to the tussock with a spade and he dug a hole right under it, and, sure enough, there was the treasure, just as the merman had said it would be. He then headed home earlier than usual, wondering if the merman was also right about his wife. He found her in the arms of the postman, just like he had been told. He ordered her out of the house, which was a hard thing for him to do, but he knew that she didn't love him and that he would be better off without her. He lived happily after that, and he was rich because of the treasure he had found, and he never again ill-treated his dog.

the Red and white Roses

I was told this story late one night in the island of Sandøy by the Faroese journalist and broadcaster, Katerin Petersen. I had been invited to the Faroes with my great friend, the Shetland storyteller Lawrence Tulloch, to do some storytelling and to coach tour guides in the art of using local stories as part of their tour. We had done a storytelling session in Sandøy, where this story was told in Faroese, and later that night, after hot whisky in Katerin's cousins' house, we went back to her house (where we were staying) and Lawrence asked her to translate the story for us. As we drank the Highland Park whisky I had brought from Orkney, she told us this story. Lawrence has written it down in his book The Foy, *but this is my version, as I remember Katerin telling it. l have since found another version of this story from Sweden.*

There was once a preacher who lived in the Faroes, and he was given his own parish to preach in. As he preached his sermon in the church his eyes fell on a lovely young woman, and his heart missed a beat. He asked her to walk out with him, and she agreed. He was blinded by her great beauty, but she was also a kind and loving person, and he enjoyed her company more and more every time they met. One day he went down on one knee and asked her to be his wife, and she agreed without a moment's hesitation. The wedding was prepared, and soon the big day was drawing near. The young woman was happy; she loved her husband-to-be very much. But there was one large black cloud on the horizon for her. The young woman had a dreadful fear of childbirth, but she knew that he would want children. She was terrified of bearing a child, and the awful pain of the labour was more than her poor mind could stand.

On the eve of her wedding the poor girl lay in her bed staring at the ceiling, and not a wink of sleep came to soothe her anguish. She thought of all the poor women who had died screaming as the child in their womb would not come out. She was so afraid of this pain that she wished that there was a way that she could be spared the agony of childbirth. Eventually she fell into a restless sleep, and she had a dream. In her dream she was shown how to avoid becoming pregnant. She had to go to the mill and turn the quernstone anti-clockwise, against the course of the sun; if she did that she would be spared the pain and danger of childbirth. She woke up in a sweat, then she hurriedly threw on some clothes and shoes and she rushed to the mill before the household woke up. She opened the door of the mill and went into the gloomy room, her heart beating as loud as thunder. With trembling hands she took hold of the handle of the quern and she turned it backwards, against the course of the sun. As she turned it she heard a loud crack come from between the stones, and this frightened her, but she carried on. A second loud crack was heard, but still she turned the quern backwards. A third crack came from the quern, and still she carried on turning it against the sun, but after

a while, when there were no more cracks, she stopped, and returned to her home and went back to bed.

The next day dawned bright and sunny, and the girl got ready for her big day. She looked as pretty as a picture when she stood by her handsome husband and took her vows. The wedding was celebrated in style, and everyone drank a happy toast to the bride and groom, and to all the children who would fill their lives with laughter and joy. But the nursery remained an empty, silent place.

One day the young woman was out walking with her husband, and they talked and laughed and everything seemed good to them. The sun was setting, and the light sent the shadows stretching a long way from their owners. The preacher stopped and looked down, and there was his shadow stretching away from him, but to his horror he saw that his wife cast no shadow.

'What have you done?' he asked her.

'I don't know what you mean,' she replied, rather startled at his question.

The preacher pointed a trembling finger towards the ground and said in a shaking voice;

'You do not cast a shadow. You must have done some evil thing to lose your shadow. What have you done?'

The young woman's mind went back to the morning of her wedding, when she had used sorcery to prevent herself from having a baby, but she denied any wrongdoing and refused to tell her husband anything about it. He was furious with her, and he dragged her home in tears.

All that evening he continued to interrogate her about why she cast no shadow. What dealing with the devil had she done to lose her shadow? The poor woman sobbed her heart out and begged for him to stop acting in this way, but he had hardened his heart towards her and he wanted answers to his questions. That night he dragged her down to the church

and he threw her inside, saying that a night locked in there might loosen her tongue. She lay on the floor sobbing until she fell asleep. When she was asleep she had a dream, which was more real than imagined. In her dream, a great black ram with a white head came to her, and it spoke to her in a terrible voice that boomed as loud as thunder. 'I am your son, had you given me the chance of life. If you had let me be born then I would have grown up to be a very important man who would have become a high court judge, but because of your witchcraft I never had that chance.'

Then he lowered his head and charged at her with his large, cruel horns. He struck her again and again, before hooking his horns through her clothes and dragging her around the church, hitting her off the pews and walls until he beat her black and blue.

When morning came the preacher went to the church to get his wife, and she staggered out in pain. He demanded to know what had happened during the night, but she refused to tell him anything. He kept pressing her, over and over again, to tell him what she had done, but she refused to answer his question. She spent the day in bed sobbing, but the preacher had no pity in his heart for her. That night he dragged her, sobbing, back to the church and locked her inside once more. She lay on the cold hard floor until she finally fell asleep. Again she had a dream, and another ram came to her, but this time it was all black with a white collar. It spoke to her with voice as loud as thunder.

'I am your second son, had you given me the chance of life. If you had let me be born then I would have grown up to be a very important man. I would have become an archbishop, but because of your witchcraft I never had that chance.'

After saying those words it attacked her with even greater ferocity than the first ram had done, until she lay there all cut and bruised and more dead than alive.

The next morning the preacher came to see

his wife, who could hardly crawl from the church to her bed. He demanded to know what had happened, but she refused to talk. He was relentless in his questioning, and any love he had once had for his wife was now replaced with hatred. That night he ignored her pleas, and he carried her back to the church and locked her inside once again. She was exhausted, and soon fell asleep. This time she had a different dream. Instead of the large, cruel rams there was a little girl. The poor little thing was terribly deformed, her arms, legs and back were twisted and she could hardly walk. She spoke to the woman in a soft and kind voice.

'I am your daughter, and I thank you for not giving me the chance of life. I am glad that you didn't allow me to be born, for I would have suffered an awful life of pain and misery, and I thank you for sparing me that.'

The little girl smiled kindly and disappeared. The woman woke up, and the tears flowed down her cheeks. While the rams were so cruel to her, they didn't hurt her as much as the sight of that poor, twisted, kind little girl. She wailed in pain, not from the cuts and bruises inflicted by the rams, but from the pain that had now filled her broken head.

The next morning when the preacher came to collect her he found her lying on the floor, nearly dead. He demanded to know what had happened, but he took her home and put her to bed. The woman wept for her daughter, that poor, strange little deformed girl who had so touched her heart. She then told her husband everything that had happened, of her fear of childbirth, her dream of turning the quern against the sun, of the terrible rams and the poor little girl. The preacher was furious with her; he had not one ounce of pity for her suffering, and there was hatred and disgust in his eyes when he looked her. As she lay there dying, she asked her husband:

'Will I ever be forgiven for what I have done? Please tell me that there will be forgiveness for me.'

He gave her a cold, hard look, and, pointing to her shoes by the side of the bed, he said;

'You will be forgiven when the laces of those shoes turn into red and white roses.'

She died soon after, a poor, broken thing.

Her husband refused to carry out the burial rites, so a preacher from outside the parish was called for, which delayed the funeral for a few days. Her poor broken body lay in a coffin in the bedroom. When they came to carry her remains to the church the men called out to the preacher to come and look at this strange thing. When the preacher entered the room he saw that there were red and white roses entwined through the lace holes of her shoes.

Toller and the good neighbours

> *There are stories like this throughout the Nordic countries that explain how the supernatural creatures left the country due to the preaching of Christianity. This is, for me, the finest version that I have yet seen, and very moving.*

There was once a big landowner who had a mansion house in the district of Lysgaard. Among his servants was a man called Toller, and he had fallen for the charms of one of the housemaids. Their courtship was sweet, and their love blossomed until they decided they would be married. The master and mistress of the house dearly loved them both, as they were hard workers and faithful servants, and so they gave them a splendid wedding dinner, and a great event it was in the big house. The master then gave Toller and his wife their wedding gift: he gave them a small cottage and some land that they could call their own. They packed their belongings and went to their new home, but it was not everyone who would have been so grateful for that piece of land. It was not a fertile spot, and the coarse brown grass of the moor stretched out in all directions, studded all over with rocks. To make matters worse, there were many ancient grave mounds in the area that people said were inhabited by the Mount-folk, as these trolls were called. But this did not bother Toller and his wife; they were sure that, with hard work and God's blessing, they could make this depressing place an oasis of plenty. Toller believed that if you were just, and did the right thing by others, then you should have nothing to fear in this world.

Late one night, Toller sat by the fire talking with his wife about what they could do to get on in the world and where to start with clearing fields and securing food for the winter. Suddenly, there was a loud knock at the door, and Toller went to see who it was that was calling so late at night. There in the doorway was a tiny old man, who said 'Good evening' as he walked into the house. Toller closed the door and went over to see who his guest was. The tiny man had long white hair and a long white beard and a large hump on his back; on his head was a bright red cap, and he wore a leather apron out of which stuck a hammer. Toller knew that this must be a troll, but he looked so kind and friendly that he was not in the least bit frightened of him. The troll looked at Toller and spoke:

'Now, hear this, Toller. I see you know what I am. I am one of the Mount-folk, who have no other place on this earth to live but in the grave mounds of the fallen warriors of old. My king has sent me here to speak to you, because he is fearful that you may bring trouble to our realm; that you may even bring about our destruction. He is keen to know what sort of a neighbour you will be to us, Toller, and to beg that you let us live in peace in this land. We will be good neighbours to you if you are the same to us.'

Toller looked at the troll and scratched his head, saying:

'You have nothing to fear from me, my good fellow. I have never harmed any of God's creatures willingly, and I think that this world

37

is big enough for all of us to live together in peace and friendship.'

The old troll man skipped around the floor in delight, saying:

'Thank you, Toller! That is the best of news! In return we will do everything that is in our power to help you, as you will see in good time.'

Toller's wife came with a bowl of creamy porridge and set it down on a stool by the window, as the troll was too small to reach the table. 'Will you take a bite of supper with us?' she asked him.

'No, thank you all the same, but I must return to the king with this great news. Good night to you both,' he said, then was out the door like a flash.

After that day the little Mount-folk were a common sight on Toller's land, going in and out of their mounds during the day, but they never did anything to upset Toller or his wife. They became so friendly that they used to trot in and out of Toller's house, and they would borrow things, like a copper kettle or a pot from the kitchen, but they always returned it sparkling clean to the same spot where they had taken it from. They worked on the land to help Toller, and by night, during the spring, they would pick all the stones off the fields and pile them neatly in a heap. At harvest time they would come out of their mounds at night and gather up all the ears of corn that had been dropped on the ground, so that Toller lost none of his crop. Toller prospered because of the Mount-folk, and in his bed at night, or in his evening prayer, he would thank God for giving him the Mount-folk as his neighbours. At Easter and Whitsuntide, and at Christmas time, he would set a large dish of creamy porridge on the mound for them to enjoy.

One day Toller's wife had some wonderful news for him: she was going to have a baby. She blossomed and grew, and soon the happy event arrived. A fine baby girl was born, but the mother suffered a lot during the childbirth,

and she became weak and ill. Toller lovingly tended his wife, and he consulted all the cunning old folk in the area who knew cures, but nothing worked. Toller sat by her bed all day and all night, tending to her every need like a loving husband should. One night Toller fell asleep through sheer exhaustion, and when he opened his eyes he saw that he was not alone; the Mount-folk were there helping out. One sat and rocked the baby's cradle, while another cleaned the room and a third was by the side of the bed giving Toller's wife a drink made of healing herbs. When they saw that Toller was awake they ran out of the room, but his wife soon made a full recovery after being given that drink.

One time Toller was worried because his horses needed new shoes, but he had no money to pay a blacksmith for the job. He said to his wife that he didn't know what to do about this, as the horses needed new shoes before he could take them into town. That night, as they lay in bed, Toller's wife asked:

'Toller, are you asleep?'

'No,' said Toller, 'what is it, my dear?'

'I think there is something wrong with the horses,' said Toller's wife, 'because there is an awful disturbance coming from the stable.' Toller threw on some clothes and took a lantern to go outside to the stable to see what was going on. As he opened the stable door a little bit he saw all the tiny Mount-folk were there shoeing his horses. They had made the horses lie down while they worked, as they were too small to reach them when they stood up. Some were taking off the old shoes, while others were filing the heads of the nails and others were nailing on the fine new shoes. Toller quietly shut the door and returned to his bed, a happy and relieved man. The next morning, when he led his horses to the water to drink, they walked on the finest shoes that he had ever seen.

The years passed, and Toller was constantly helped by his good neighbours, and they both tried to help one another out whatever way they could. Toller grew old, and his daughter, Inger, grew up to be a fine young woman. The farm was no longer rough moorland, but fine fields of grass and corn. His cottage had been pulled down many years before, and now he had a fine large house that they lived in.

Life had indeed been good to Toller and his wife, thanks to the Mount-folk.

Late one night there was a knock at Toller's door, and there stood the Mount-man who had first visited him, but he was not dressed in his usual fashion. He wore a shaggy cap on his head and a woollen neckerchief around his throat, while his body was covered by a large sheep-skin cloak and he carried a staff in his hand. His face was a mask of sorrow as he said:

'I have an invitation from the king. He wants you, your wife and little Inger to come to the Mount, as he has something of great importance that he wishes to discuss with you.'

As he said that, the tears rolled down the Mount-man's cheeks, and no matter how hard he tried, Toller couldn't comfort him. The Mount-man would not say what the matter was, just that they should go and see the king at once. Toller, his wife and daughter left the house with the Mount-man and went to the Mount.

The door of the Mount was standing wide open, and Toller, his wife and daughter followed the Mount-man down the passage that led into the heart of the mound. Inside, they saw that the hall was decorated with sweet willow, crowsfoot and other wildflowers, while a long table was set with a great feast. Toller and his family were sat next to the king at the top of the table, and all the Mount-folk took their places and started to eat. Instead of their usual cheery selves, they ate in silence, and every now and again they would sigh and shake their heads, and their faces glistened with tears. When they had finished, the king said to Toller:

'I invited you here this evening to thank you

for being so kind to us, and for being such a good neighbour. Many mortal men would not have treated us with such respect and trust as you have, and we thank you for that. But, sadly, our time has passed, and we must leave this land for good. There have been so many new churches built in Denmark, and they have such large bells that ring so loudly every morning and evening, that we can no longer bear to live here. We are leaving this place tonight and travelling across Jutland to the coast, where we will cross over the sea to Norway, just as many of our people have done in the past. There we can find quiet solitude, and live without fear of church bells or prayers. We would now like to wish you farewell, and to give a blessing to you and your family, Toller.'

The king rose from his seat, and the other Mount-folk did the same, and they filed out of the Mount and out into the night. They took Toller and his wife by the hands, and said their final goodbye to them as they passed. When the king came to Toller's daughter, he said:

'To you, dear Inger, we will give something that will help you to remember the little Mount-folk when they are far away from you. It is our blessing, child. Remember us.'

Every one of the little Mount-folk took a stone and dropped it into Inger's apron as they passed by her on their final journey from Denmark.

Toller, with his wife and daughter, climbed to the top of the Mount and watched the tiny figures of the Mount-folk as they walked away into the moonlight. Each one carried a wallet on their back and had a staff in their hand. When they had almost vanished from sight they stopped, turned and waved their little arms in farewell to Toller and his family, then they were gone. With a heavy heart Toller, his wife and little Inger returned to their house, which now seemed as silent as the tomb.

The next morning, when Inger awoke, she saw something shining in her room. When she went to look to see what it was, all the stones that the Mount-folk had given her had turned into brightly coloured precious gems. There were all sorts of colours of all shades: blue, brown, white, green and black. The Mount-folk had given each stone the colour of their own eyes, so that Inger would remember them when she looked at the gems. All the precious stones that we see today sparkle and shine only because the Mount-folk gave them the colour of their eyes, and they originally came from the stones that little Inger got from the Mount-folk so that she would remember them.

the elf maiden

This story has long been a favourite of mine. The book that I have it in says that it is from Lapland, and I am assuming that it is the province from the north of Sweden, but it could be Finnish.

There were once two young men who lived in a village in the north of Lapland. These young men were friends, but a rivalry arose between them when they both fell in love with the same girl. In the winter, the sun deserted them and hid its face for months on end, so that it was forever darkness. The only light there was came from the beautiful colours of the Northern Lights as they danced across the sky, sending curtains of brightly coloured light cascading and shimmering down from the heavens. The two young men would try to tempt the girl to leave her parents' house and to go on a sleigh ride over the snow and frozen lakes. The horse's breath would burst from its mouth like white summer clouds in the freezing cold air, and the sleigh bells would jingle merrily as they sped over the countryside that was illuminated by the Northern Lights. They would also invite her to join them at the dances held in their neighbours' barns, and they passed the winter wooing the object of their desires.

When winter loosened its deadly grip on the world and the sun started to peep once more above the horizon, then the hearts of the people were gladdened. They started to repair the great nets that they would use that summer in the fishing grounds far away in the north. When the time came, the villagers set off to sail to the islands that lay to the north, where they had fishing huts built for them to live in while they caught the fish that were to

be the following winter's food. The two young men and the girl ended up living together with some of their friends in one of these huts, and they also worked together on the same boat. Now, the one young man started to notice that the girl paid far more attention to his rival than she did to him, but he pushed all such thoughts from his mind and carried on trying to impress her. As the weeks passed, it became obvious to him that the girl had made her choice and that he was the unlucky one, and so his thoughts turned from love to revenge. He plotted the destruction of his rival, and a wicked plan formed in his head, but it would have to wait for some months before he could carry it out. As the time passed he grew happier with the evil plan, but he was all smiles and kindness to his former friend, so that he suspected nothing.

Finally, the day arrived when he could take out his awful revenge on the rival who had stolen away his girl. The boats were getting ready to leave the fishing station for the year, and everything was packed away safely for another season. The island would soon be left to the wild birds and beasts, and to the cruel north wind. The wicked young man delayed the boat from sailing until all the others had left, and then he said in a pitiful voice:

'Oh dear, where's my best knife? I've left it back in the hut.'

He turned to his former friend, and with a

43

friendly smile he asked him; 'Friend, could you please run back to the hut and see if you can find my knife, while I pull up the anchor and unleash the tiller ready for our journey home?'

'Why, yes, of course I can,' said the other man, who suspected nothing, and he ran back to the hut.

There he found the knife on the windowsill, right where his rival had set it, and he put it in his pocket and ran back to the boat, but by the time that he arrived on the shore the boat was already well out to sea. He was stranded alone on the island with no hope of rescue until the following summer, but with no food for the winter he knew that he was already as good as dead. He cursed the treachery of his so-called friend, but swore that he would survive until the following summer so that he could have his revenge on him.

He then went off to a part of the island that wasn't quite as bare as the rest of it, and where a clump of small trees was growing. He used the knife to cut down a small tree, which he carved into a bow for himself. He strung it with some twine that he found in the hut, and he used it to hunt seabirds, which he skinned and ate for his supper.

He lived this way until Christmas Eve came around. He thought sadly of the previous Christmas Eve, when he had danced with his love and the world had seemed a kinder place to him. He went to the shore to gather driftwood for the fire, and see if any small trees had been blown down by the gales, and he brought the wood home and piled it by the door of the hut for the following day. He looked longingly towards the distant shore of the mainland, just visible by the ghostly flickering of the Northern Lights. Then he saw it: a boat! A boat was sailing towards the island. Could it be his family and friends come at last to look for him? Had his rival confessed his crime and sent out a search party? All these thought raced through his mind, but as the boat drew nearer he saw that it was not a kind of boat he had ever seen before. It landed on the shore, and a group of beautiful people jumped laughing onto the frosty rand and started to walk towards the hut. He knew that these were no mortal creatures: they were not of his kind, they were elves, and he hid behind the wood pile. The strangers drew closer; their laughter and voices rang as clear as crystal bells in the frosty air. They all carried provisions with them, and they all went into the hut to celebrate the Yule in their own fashion. Then the young man saw two beautiful girls, more beautiful and better dressed than the others, and each girl carried a large basket of food and drink. He was captivated by their beauty, but fear kept him hidden from their gaze.

A short time later the same two girls slipped out of the hut in order to explore the island. The elves have keen sight, and one of the girls saw the young man hiding behind the wood pile. She stared at him for a moment, and then said:

'What a strange creature. I wonder what it's made of?' and she pinched the man on the arm.

But he had a pin stuck into his jacket sleeve, and the point ran into the elf maiden's finger and drew blood. She screamed loudly, and all the other elves rushed out to see what the matter was. When they saw the terrified man crouching behind the wood pile they turned and fled back to their boat, taking their provisions with them. Soon they had gone, but to his amazement the beautiful young elf maiden whose finger had been pricked stood there helpless and pale. She spoke to him; her voice was like frozen silver.

'You will have to make me your wife,' she said, 'for you have drawn my blood, and I belong to you.'

The young man agreed happily to have her as his wife, and it was settled.

'But,' said the young man, 'how shall we live until next summer?

'Don't be afraid of such things,' said the elf maiden, 'for if you marry me you will be all right. I am rich, and so are my family, and we will be well provided for over the winter months.'

The elf maiden was as good as her word, and there was never any shortage of food for them during the winter months. Food was always on the table, and he knew better than to ask her how it got there.

The months passed, and the north wind lost its frozen bite as once more the sun arrived. Soon the villagers would return to the island in their fishing boats. One day the elf maiden said to the man;

'Where shall we go to live?'

'I don't care where we go," replied the man, 'where do you think?'

'I think we should go away to the far side of the island,' she said, 'far away from the fisher folk's huts.'

And so they left and walked to the other end of the island, far away from where his own people would soon be returning. They looked for a place that was both sheltered and had a stream nearby or water. After a long walk they found such a place, a beautiful sheltered spot where the wind didn't howl and that had a stream running by it to provide them with cool, sweet water. Then they found a place where the moss grew deep, and they lay down there to spend the night. 'Now,' said the elf maiden, 'if you hear strange noises in the night, don't look to see what it is. Don't move, just ignore it and we will be fine.'

'Oh, what noises are we likely to hear in this quiet place?' enquired the man, and they soon fell asleep in each other's arms.

During the night the man was woken by loud noises – of sawing and hammering and the sound of building work going on right next to them, as if every builder in the world was there – but he remembered his wife's warning and he didn't look to see what it was. In the morning, to his amazement, there stood the most beautiful wooden house, right where they wanted their home to be. The man rushed around the house, and it was lovely.

He grabbed the elf maiden by the waist and he twirled her around, laughing like a madman. They breakfasted on wild cherries in their new house, and then the elf maiden said, 'Now then, you must select a spot to build a cowshed. Mark out a fair-sized one, not too big and not too small.' The man wondered why they should bother, but he did as he was told, as he knew that his wife possessed strange powers and he respected what she had to say. He marked out an area that seemed reasonable, and later they went to bed. He was woken up during the night with the same strange sound of building work, and in the morning there stood a fine new cowshed, complete with milking pails and stools. His wife then asked him to measure out a place for a storehouse, as big as he wanted, and so he did this, and it, too, was built in one night.

When their fine new farm was complete the elf maiden suggested that they should go and visit her family, which the man agreed to happily. Off they went to her parents' house, where they were greeted warmly. All the neighbours gathered there, and they feasted and played for days on end. After a while the young couple were growing bored with playing, and wanted to return home. Before they left the elf maiden whispered to her husband:

'Now, be quick and leap over the threshold, or it will be worse for you.'

He did as his wife told him, and sprang over the threshold of the house like an arrow from a bow. Just at that moment his father-in-law threw a huge hammer at him, which would have broken his legs had it struck him, but it missed its mark.

As they walked home the elf maiden said to her husband:

'You will hear strange sounds coming behind us, but you must not look around until you step through the door of our house.'

Soon he heard the sound of feet trampling on the road behind them, but he did not look around. When he reached his own door, and his hand was on the door latch, he thought that it was safe to look, and he turned around to see what had made all the noise. There he saw a huge herd of cattle coming through the gate into the field. Half were already inside, and they were happily grazing on the grass by the banks of the stream, but the ones that were still outside the gate melted away and vanished from sight. Had he waited he would have got all of them; a gift from his father-in-law to his daughter for outwitting him. The cattle they had got were still a great herd, and he was now a very rich man.

The man and the elf maiden lived happily together, but there were times when she would vanish without telling him where she was going or what she had been doing. He remained silent for a while, and then one day he asked her why she went away. She replied;

'My dear, I am bound to go, even if it is against my will, but there is only one way to stop me. Drive a nail into the threshold of the door, and then I will never be able to pass in or out.'

He drove a nail into the threshold, and she remained with him for the rest of his days.

HOW TAM SCOTT LOST HIS SIGHT

> *It was believed that the fin folk lived on a beautiful floating island called Hildaland during the summer months. Strange, floating islands have been seen in Orkney, lying where no island should be. This illusion is caused by refracted light in summer bringing into view a distant image that is usually out of sight. I myself saw Hildaland quite clearly during the early 1980s. I had gone to the farm of Valdigar in Tankerness, where I was born, for Sunday dinner with the family. After a fine meal of Orkney beef, I went for a walk around the shore with two of my brothers. One of my brothers had with him a pair of binoculars that he had just bought and wanted to try out. While on the seashore, below Kirkwall Airport, we saw a strange island lying just off the east coast of Shapinsay. We looked at it through the binoculars and saw that it had a large, grey, two-storey building on it, but no other buildings were visible. We had never seen that island before, yet we were all born beside that bay and knew the area intimately. As we watched, the island started to melt away; first the west end started to vanish, then the bottom of the island started to go, until it looked as though it was floating above the sea. After about fifteen or twenty minutes it was gone, and we never saw it again.*

Tam Scott was as good a sailor as ever pulled on an oar or walked the deck of a sailing ship, but that was before he lost his sight, of course. In this life we meet many people, some good and some bad, but there are many foul hearts hidden beneath a fair face, as Tam found to his cost. This is the story of how Tam Scott lost his sight.

It was August, and the Lammas Fair was being held in Kirkwall. That great market was one of the highlights of the year in Orkney, and traders and visitors from Caithness and Shetland would come to Kirkwall to buy and sell their produce; everything from a horse to a hen's leg could be bought, and everywhere the sound of laughter filled the air. The booths were set up under the shadow of St Magnus Cathedral, that great red sandstone church built to commemorate an earl who was slaughtered long ago. Tam Scott sailed into Kirkwall harbour with his boatload of passengers from his native island of Sanday. He smiled when he noticed that some of the young girls had the sign of the cross marked on their chests by their over-protective mothers in case the evil fin folk should try to upset the boat and claim the girls as their brides. The fin folk are creatures that live in a fine city under the sea called Finfolkaheem, and on islands called Hildaland that float on the surface of the sea in summertime, and they are always on the lookout for mortal women to be their wives. Tam tied up the boat with his friend, Willie Muir, and then the two men wandered off through the streets of Kirkwall in search of some fun. After a while, Tam met a tall man with black hair, a thick black beard and dark, cold eyes.

Anna Anglemark

'Good morning to you, Tam,' said the man.

'Good morning to you, said Tam, 'but I'm sorry, I can't say that I know who you are.'

'That's of no importance,' said the man, 'but I'm in need of a favour from you. I have a cow that I need taken to one of the North Isles in your boat, but I'll pay you double the cost since I'm taking you away from the fair so early.'

Thinking of the money, Tam agreed, and hurried off to find his friend Willie so that they could get the boat ready. Tam found Willie lying at the head of the Anchor Close, dead drunk, so he gave him a kick and a curse, and then set off to the boat to get her ready to sail. Shortly after, the dark-featured man came leading a fine cow behind him. When he reached the boat Tam went to help him get the cow on board, but the man just lifted up the cow as though it was a sheep, and he set her down in the boat. Tam was amazed, saying, 'Well, you were not the last in the queue when strength was being dished out,' but the man said nothing.

Tam cast off the rope and steered the boat out of the harbour and headed north past Thieves Holm.

'Where are we going?' asked Tam.

'East of Shapinsay,' replied the man.

Tam steered his boat through the strong currents of the String before rounding the east side of the island of Shapinsay.

'Where to now?' asked Tam.

'East of Stronsay,' came the reply, and Tam turned his boat eastwards.

Now, Tam Scott was a cheery soul and he liked a good laugh, so he tried to talk to the stranger, but he got no joy from his passenger. All the man would say at Tam's attempts at being friendly was:

'A close tongue keeps a safe head.'

When they rounded the east side of the island of Stronsay, Tam said:

'You will be wanting to land in Sanday then?'

'East of Sanday,' was the reply.

'East of Sanday? said Tam, 'Surely you are making some mistake; the only thing east of Sanday is Norway, and my boat is too small to sail there safely.'

'A close tongue keeps a safe head,' came the reply.

Now, as they sailed to the east of Sanday, a great bank of fog rose from the sea, but it shone as though the rising sun was behind it. Tam was worried:

'We had better turn back, because I don't like the look of that fog.'

'A close tongue keeps a safe head,' replied the man.

'That may be true,' said Tam, 'but a close fog won't be too good for either of us.'

By this time the fog had swallowed them up, but it glowed with a strange golden light, the like of which Tam had never seen before. After a while the fog lifted and, to Tam's amazement, there in front of them was the most beautiful island he had ever seen. He had no idea where it was, because he didn't recognise it, but the fields were as green as emeralds and the corn shone like spun gold. Tam guessed that this had to be Hildaland that he was seeing, and that the dark-featured stranger was a fin man. The fin man sprang to the stern of the boat where Tam sat and said:

'I must blindfold you now. Don't give me any trouble and no harm will come to you.'

Tam remembered how the fin man had picked up the cow in Kirkwall, and he put up no resistance as the fin man tied Tam's own neckerchief around his eyes.

Soon the boat grounded on a gravel beach, and many strange voices could be heard all around as the cow was carried out of the boat. Then Tam heard a sound that made his head swim, because on the shore sat some mermaids, who started to sing their song of enchantment. Tam could see them sitting on the shore, as the neckerchief had not fully covered both his eyes, and their beauty far outshone anything he had ever seen in his life before. Mermaids are always on the lookout for a human husband, and they competed with each other to win his heart with their enchanted song. Tam was in a dream as the lovely music lifted his spirits and filled his heart with joy and longing, but the fin man was not so easily impressed.

'Go on, clear off, you lot,' he ordered, 'this man is married and has children in the island of Sanday.'

Then the music changed from a song of joy to one of bitter regret and sorrow, which made the tears flow down Tam's cheeks.

Once the boat was unloaded, the fin man threw a bag of money at Tam's feet, and pushed the boat off from the shore, against the course of the sun, as the fin folk are heathens and in league with the Devil.

'Keep steering straight ahead and you will soon be home,' ordered the fin man, as the boat headed back towards the fog bank.

Tam tore off the blindfold, but the shining fog had once more engulfed the boat and he could see nothing of the island. He picked up the bag of money, and sure enough he had been well paid, but every coin was made of copper, as the fin folk love silver too much to be parted from it. Soon Tam found himself leaving the mysterious shining fog, and there in front of him was the island of Sanday. He steered his boat homewards, and was thankful to be returning to his family safe and well once more.

A year passed, and it was once again time to carry passengers south to the Lammas Fair in Kirkwall. Tam would often wish that he had stayed in his bed that day instead of going there. He had secured his boat in Kirkwall harbour, and headed up the street to see what he could see. He took a drink with old friends, and it was a fine day. Then he saw him: the mysterious stranger that he had ferried to Hildaland the previous year. Tam walked over to him and said in a friendly voice:

'How are you? It's good to see you! Would you like to have a drink of ale with me? How have you been since I saw you last?'

A black look passed over the fin man's face, and he took from his pocket something that resembled a snuffbox. He opened the box and said:

'Did you ever see me?' and with that he blew some of the contents right into Tam's eyes. 'You will never have to say that you saw me again.'

The silvery powder stung Tam's eyes and he cried out with pain, and then the sight left his eyes and he was plunged into a world of darkness for the rest of his days. Never again did Tam see the sweet light of day, nor his wife's loving smile or his children growing up. As I said, there is many a foul heart hidden beneath a fair face, and you should not make too free with people that you do not know.

the trolls and the bear

> Trolls were in the habit of disturbing people on Christmas Eve, but in this version it was all the year round. I know of a German version of this story where a water sprite takes up residence in a watermill and causes misery for the miller.

In the parish of Rumskulla there was an estate called Norrhult, but a long time ago it was plagued by all sorts of horrible trolls. These trolls treated the house as their own, and created such havoc every night that the people decided that they could not suffer living there any longer. One day they gathered all their things together and abandoned the house and went to stay with neighbours. There was one old man who remained behind, because he was too old and feeble to make the journey, and the trolls made his life a misery. They poked him and prodded him and pinched him with their long black fingernails till he was black and blue, and they tried to get him to eat their disgusting food. This seemed to amuse the trolls, but the old man was less than happy about it.

One evening, there was a knock at the door and the old man answered it. There stood a fine, strong young man leading a bear on a chain.

'Can I come in?' asked the man, 'I am a weary travelling showman, and this is my performing bear. Don't be scared of him, he will do anything I tell him to. We would appreciate a roof over our heads tonight, if you would be so kind.'

The old man was delighted to have human company, but he thought it only fair to warn the young man about the trolls.

'My friend,' the old man said, 'you are welcome to stay, but you may not want to after I tell you about the curse that there is on this place. Every night, just after dark, the most horrible, ugly and evil trolls gather here, and they cause a terrible disturbance.'

'Oh, never mind,' said the young man, 'I am not scared by trolls; I'll take my chances here this night.'

And so the man made a bed for himself near to where the old man slept, and the bear lay down beside him.

After darkness fell, just as the old man had said, the door burst open and in came the most horrible-looking bunch of trolls that has ever been gathered together in one place. They built up the fire until it burnt as hot as a furnace, so hot in fact that you would have thought that the house would be set ablaze. One of the trolls set a huge pot over the fire, and they began to fill it with all sorts of filthy things that trolls love to eat. They had lizards, frogs and toads, worms, slugs, snails – all manner of horrible things. Once they were cooked, the trolls set the table and sat down to eat.

One troll threw a worm to the bear and said in a loud, stupid voice:

'Would you like a fishy, kitty puss?'

Another troll ambled over to where the young man lay and held out a dish of filthy slime, and asked him:

'Would you like some supper?'

The young man sprang to his feet and unchained the bear. It roared so loudly that the trolls stopped eating, and then it sprang at them, beating them with its huge paws. It knocked the trolls this way and that, and soon they had all fled from the house screaming.

'Well, that certainly gave them a fright," said the young man, and they started to clear out all the filthy, stinking food from the house.

After a while one of the trolls peeped around the door; he had a mouth that was so wide that he could have whispered in his own ear, but the young man pointed to him and shouted 'Get him!', and the bear went roaring after him.

The following morning the young man gathered together all the villagers and neighbours and told them that the only way to protect themselves from the trolls was to have a cross erected on the estate. They should also have a prayer cut into the side of Cross Mountain, because that was where the trolls lived. Once they had done that, they would be free from the trolls. They thanked the young man, and carried out his orders.

Seven years later, a man from the Norrhult estate went to Norrköping on business. When he was walking home that night he heard the sound of a horse's hooves on the road behind him. A fine man on a black horse stopped beside him and asked him:

'Where are you going?'

'I'm going to Norrhult, sir,' replied the man.

'Well, jump up behind me on the horse and I'll take you with me,' said the man, 'I'm a neighbour of yours, so it's not taking me off my road.'

The man jumped up on the back of the horse and held tight to the stranger. The horse galloped along so swiftly that the man thought that they must be making good progress. In fact, the horse was not running along the road, but was galloping through the air, but it was too dark for the man to see. Suddenly, the horse stumbled, but the man held on tight to the stranger and didn't fall off.

'It's a good thing that you are holding on to me so tightly,' said the stranger, 'as that was the top of the steeple of Linköping's cathedral that the horse caught his hoof on.'

They rode on through the sky, and the stranger asked the man who was clinging on behind him:

'Tell me, I visited Norrhult seven years ago and I seem to remember that you had a very vicious cat. Is it still alive?'

'Oh, yes indeed, sir,' said the man, guessing that the rider was a troll, 'it is still alive, and there are many more of them.'

After riding for a while longer, the man pulled on the reins and the horse stopped. The Norrhult man climbed down from the horse and found himself at Cross Mountain, very near his home.

A while later another troll arrived at Norrhult and peeped around the door.

'Do you still have that big savage cat?' it asked.

'Watch out!' replied the man, 'She is lying by the fire with seven young ones beside her, and they are far more savage than she is.'

'Oh, no!' cried the troll, and ran away into the darkness. After that time, there were no more trolls seen at Norrhult.

east of the sun and west of the moon

> This is one of the greatest tales of the Norwegian folk-tale collector's – Peter Christen Asbjørnsen and Jørgen Moe'. There is another version of this story collected by them in Norway, and there is also a Swedish version of this marvellous 'wonder tale'.

There was once a man who lived with his family in a small house among the trees. He was very poor, and he had a large family to support, so he worked hard to earn enough money to put food on the table for his wife and children. While his children were dressed in nothing but rags, they were all very pretty, but his youngest daughter was the prettiest of them all. Her beauty shone so bright that it shamed the sun, and she had the sweetest nature of any girl in the country.

Late one Thursday evening, the family all sat around the fire to keep warm as they carried out all sorts of tasks that needed to be done. Outside, the wind howled like a hungry wolf, while the rain beat against the window pane like watery fists. Suddenly, there came a loud tapping at the window: three loud taps that made them all jump with fright. The man went outside to see who it was, but instead of a traveller looking for shelter from the storm, there stood a huge white bear.

'Good evening, my good man,' said the bear.

'G-g-good evening to you too,' said the man, who was shaking in his boots.

'Don't be afraid of me,' said the white bear, 'I mean you no harm. I want to make a deal with you.'

'Oh,' said the man, 'what could I offer you, because I have nothing in the world?'

'I want you to give me your youngest daughter,' said the bear, 'and in return I will make you rich beyond your wildest dreams.'

'Well, I would love to be rich and never to have to worry about feeding my family again,' said the man, 'but I will have to go inside to see what my family thinks'

The man went back indoors and told the startled family about the huge white bear that was outside, and his offer of riches in return for the youngest daughter. The girl was horrified, and refused to go with the bear, so the man went back outside to where the bear was waiting.

'I've got a bit of a problem,' said the man to the bear, 'you see, my daughter's not too keen on the idea. But if you give me a week, I'm sure I can change her mind.'

'All right,' said the white bear, 'I will return at the same hour next Thursday evening,' and with that he turned around and walked back into the forest.

The poor man now urged his daughter to change her mind and to go with the white bear. He told her of all the riches that they would enjoy, and how they would never have to go hungry or dress in rags again. He said that if the white bear had riches to give them, imagine how rich he must be himself, and she would live like a queen. No more back-breaking toil in return for a few copper coins, no more scrimping and saving to provide for the family. Now they could have servants to do the work, and they would be respected by everyone. The girl knew that if she still refused then she was condemning her family to a future of hardship and poverty, so, with a heavy heart, she finally agreed to go with the white bear.

The following Thursday evening there came three loud taps at the window pane, and the girl stood up, and, with tears in her eyes, she said goodbye to her mother and father, sisters and brothers. She went outside with her father, carrying her few meagre possessions in a small bundle, and there stood the huge white bear.

The white bear told her to climb up on his back, and he walked away with the girl and disappeared among the trees.

'Are you afraid?' asked the bear.

'No, I'm not afraid,' said the girl.

'Then hold on tightly to my shaggy coat,' said the bear, 'and no harm will come to you.'

The white bear walked on for a long, long time until he eventually arrived at the side of a very steep hill. He gave a loud knock on the side of the hill and it opened up so that the bear could walk inside. There, in the hill, stood a magnificent castle, and when the bear walked through the doorway and went inside, all the rooms glittered with gold, silver and precious gems. The young girl stood rooted to the floor, dumbstruck by the riches that surrounded her. In the grand dining room there stood a table covered with dishes of all sorts of fine food, and silver goblets of all sorts of drink.

'Sit down and eat,' said the bear, 'you must be hungry after your long journey'

The bear gave the girl a beautiful silver bell.

'Take this bell, and whatever you desire, just ring it and you will have it in a moment,' said the bear, and he left her alone to eat her fill.

After her meal, the girl felt tired and wanted to go to bed. She picked up the silver bell and rang it, and before she knew what had happened, she found herself in a beautiful bedchamber that was decorated with gold and silver, and there was a four-poster bed waiting for her. The sheets and pillows were made of pure white silk, and the canopy of the bed was also of white silk, with a gold fringe around the edge. The girl slipped into bed and sank into its warm softness and was soon fast asleep. During the night, she woke up to find that she was not alone, for a man had entered the bedchamber and got into bed beside her. She wasn't afraid, as she could feel in her heart that he was a good man, but it was too dark to see him. It was, in fact, the white bear, who could change his form into that of a man at night. In the morning, before the sun rose, the mysterious man left the bedchamber and was gone. Every day the girl wandered through the empty castle on her own, or sometimes with the white bear as company, but every night the strange man crept into the bed beside her, but she never saw what he looked like.

One day, the white bear asked her if she was feeling all right, as she had been getting more and more withdrawn and silent.

'I am missing my mother and father, and my brothers and sisters,' said the girl. 'If I could just see that they were all right, I would be happy.'

'Well,' said the bear, 'I can take you home to visit them, and that would cure your unhappiness, but you must first promise me one thing.'

'Anything!' said the girl, 'I will promise to do anything you want, if I can only see my family again.' '

All right,' said the bear, 'I will take you there, but first you have to promise not to talk alone with your mother. Only talk to her when the others are around. She will take you by the hand and try to lure you into a room to talk to you alone, but you must refuse. If you don't do as I say, then it will bring about nothing but bad luck for the both of us.'

'I promise not to do that," said the girl, and the visit was arranged for the following Sunday.

When the day that they were to go and visit the girl's parents arrived, she climbed up onto the white bear's back and he set off at a brisk pace. After a while they arrived at a great mansion house, which was where her family now lived. Her brothers and sisters were outside in the garden playing games, while the servants ran around tending to their every need.

'Now don't forget your promise,' said the bear, 'or it will spell disaster for us both.'

'Don't worry,' said the girl, 'I won't forget.'

The girl had a happy reunion with her family, and they each admired the grand clothes that they now wore instead of rags. They all thanked her for bringing about this change in their lives, and they wanted to know how her life was with the white bear. The day passed as happy as could be, but the girl's mother always tried to lure her into her bedchamber so that they could talk alone, just as the bear said she would; but the girl found excuses not to go. Finally, the mother got her way, and the girl went into the room to talk to her alone. The mother pressed her to tell her all about her life with the bear, and eventually the girl told her mother everything: how she walked around the castle alone all day, and how lonely she was. She told her about the strange man who slept with her every night, but who she never saw. The mother was horrified.

'You might be sleeping with a troll for all that you know,' declared her mother. 'Take this small piece of tallow candle home with you, and when he is asleep you can light it and look to see his face. But be careful not to allow any of the melting tallow to drip onto him.'

The girl took the small piece of tallow candle and slipped it down the front of her dress to take home with her. As the evening wore away, the white bear returned for her, and she said goodbye to her family. As she rode back to the castle on the white bear's back, he asked her,

'Did your mother try to talk to you alone?'

'Well, I would be lying if I said that she didn't,' replied the girl.

'Well, remember what I warned you,` said the bear. 'If you listened to your mother's advice

then it will bring great misfortune on us both, and everything that there ever was between us will be broken into nothingness'

'No,' said the girl, 'I didn't listen to her advice.'

It was late when they reached the castle in the hill, and the girl went to bed. Later that night, as usual, she could feel the man slip into bed next to her. She waited until she was sure that he was sleeping, and then she thought about the candle she had brought back with her. As carefully and silently as she could, she slipped out of the bed and fetched the tallow candle. Her hand trembled as she lit the candle and held it up so that the light fell on the sleeping man. There, illuminated by the warm light of the candle, lay a prince sleeping contentedly. His hair shone like spun gold in the candlelight, and his face was so handsome and finely featured that her heart filled with love for him and she felt an overpowering urge to kiss him. She bent silently over the sleeping prince and kissed him softly on the cheek, but, as she did so, three drops of hot tallow fell onto the prince's shirt. He awoke with a start and saw the girl standing over him with the candle in her hand.

'What have you done?' he cried. 'You have brought great misfortune to us both! If you had only waited for this year to pass, then I would have been free of this curse and we could have lived together in love and happiness for the rest of our days, but everything between us is now broken and can never be mended. I am a prince, but my mother died and my father married a woman who was a witch. She cast a spell on me that turned me into a white bear during the day and a man at night. If I could have slept by your side during the night for a year then the spell would have been broken, and we could have been married, but now I must return to her. She lives in a castle that lies East of the Sun and West of the Moon, where she has a troll princess who has a nose three ells long, and it is to this creature that I now must be married.'

The girl clutched him by his legs and the tears rolled down her cheeks.

'Can I not come with you?' she asked.

'No, you cannot,' replied the prince.

'Then tell me the way that I must go,' begged the girl, 'and I will search for you.'

'Yes, you may search for me,' said the prince, 'but there is no way of reaching that place. It lies East of the Sun and West of the Moon, but it is not possible for you to ever go there.'

'I love you,' sobbed the girl, shaking with the pain that ran through her body from her broken heart, 'and I will find a way. Somehow I must.'

The next morning, when the girl woke up, both the white bear and the castle were gone. She found herself lying on a green patch of ground in the middle of a large gloomy wood, and by her side lay the small bundle of rags that she had brought with her. She sat there and sobbed for a long time, wishing that she had only listened to the bear and not to her mother. After a while she stood up and walked away. She had no idea where to go, so she just walked on and on, day after day. She eventually came to a tall rocky crag that soared above her head, and under the crag there sat an old hag who was playing with a golden apple. She tossed the apple high up in the air and caught it again, and she watched the girl as she approached.

'Good morning,' said the girl, 'please, can you help me? I am looking for the castle that lies East of the Sun and West of the Moon, where a prince lives with his evil stepmother and a troll princess who has a nose three ells long and who is to be his bride.'

'Oh,' said the hag, 'how do you know about him? Maybe you are the girl who should have been his bride?'

'Yes,' said the girl in a sad voice, 'I am she.'

'Ah, is that so?' said the hag, 'well, well, it was you was it? All I know of the prince is that he lives in the castle that is East of the Sun and West of the Moon, and you may get there some day or never. I don't know the way, but take my horse and ride to my neighbour; she

may be able to tell you how to get there. Just give the horse a pat under the left ear and tell him to run along home, and he will do as you say.' The hag tossed the golden apple to the girl, saying 'Here, take this with you, it may come in useful one day.'

The girl thanked the hag and rode away on the horse to visit her neighbour.

The horse brought the girl to another crag, under which sat another old hag, who was carding wool with a pair of golden carding-combs. The girl patted the horse under the ear and sent it home, then asked the second hag if she knew how to get to the prince who lived in the castle that lay East of the Sun and West of the Moon.

'Ah,' said the second hag, 'maybe you are the girl who should have been his bride?'

'Yes,' said the girl sadly, 'I am she.'

'Well,' said the hag, 'I only know that it lies East of the Sun and West of the Moon, and that you may get there some day or never. You can borrow my horse and ride to my neighbour; she may be able to help you. Just pat the horse under the left ear when you get there and tell him to run along home, and he will do as you say.'

The hag gave the girl her pair of golden carding-combs.

'Here, you can take these with you,' said the second hag, 'they may come in useful one day.'

After thanking the second hag, the girl rode on to another high crag, under which sat a third hag, who sat spinning with a golden spinning-wheel. She greeted her, like the others, and asked her if she knew how to get to the castle that lay East of the Sun and West of the Moon.

'Ah, maybe you are the girl who should have been the young prince's bride?' asked the third hag.

'Yes,' said the girl sadly, 'I am she.'

'Well,' said the hag. 'I only know that the castle lies East of the Sun and West of the

Moon, and you may get there some day or never. You can borrow my horse and ride to see the East Wind; he may know the way and will be able to blow you in the right direction. Just pat the horse under the left ear when you get there and tell him to run along home, and he will do as you say.'

The hag gave the girl the golden spinning-wheel.

'Here, take this with you,' said the third hag, 'it might come in useful one day.'

So the girl thanked the third hag and rode off to see the East Wind.

The girl rode on, day after day, until eventually the horse brought her to the house of the East Wind.

'East Wind,' said the girl, 'I am looking for the prince who lives in the castle that lies East of the Sun and West of the Moon. Do you know where that is?'

'I have heard of the prince, and the castle,' said the East Wind, 'but I have never blown so far. Climb up on my back and we will go to see my brother, the West Wind. He is much stronger than I am, and he might know the way.'

The girl climbed up on the East Wind's back, and he set off at great speed until they arrived at the house of the West Wind.

When they arrived at the house, they both went inside.

'Hello brother,' said the East Wind. 'I have here the girl who should have married the prince who lives in the castle that lies East of the Sun and West of the Moon. Do you know how to get there?'

'No,' said the West Wind, 'I have never blown so far as that. But I will take her to see our brother, the South Wind, because he is much stronger than either of us and has travelled far and wide.'

So the girl climbed up onto the West Wind's back, and he flew with great speed to the house of the South Wind.

'Hello brother,' said the West Wind. 'this is the girl who should have married the prince who lives in the castle that lies East of the Sun and West of the Moon. Do you know where that is?'

'So, you are the one who should have married the prince,' said the South Wind. 'Well, I myself have never blown so far as to see that castle, but I will take you to our brother, the North Wind. He is older and far stronger than any of us, and he has blustered all over the world. If he doesn't know, then there is nobody in the world that could tell you.'

The girl thanked the South Wind and climbed up onto his back, and he set off at great speed for the house of the North Wind.

When they got near to the North Wind's house he saw them coming, and he was wild and raging and yelled at them.

'Blast the two of you! What do you want with me?'

His cold icy breath chilled the girl to the bone, and she was frightened by his wild manner.

'Now, now, there's no need to be like that! It is I, your brother the South Wind, and I have the girl who should have married the prince who lives in the castle that lies East of the Sun and West of the Moon. Do you know how to get there?'

'Yes,' roared the Wind, 'I know where it is well enough; I once blew an aspen leaf there many, many years ago. It is so far away that I had to rest for days before I was strong enough to return home. If you are brave enough to come with me, I will take you there on my back. But only if you really desire it."

'Oh, I do,' cried the girl. 'Yes; I truly do, with all my heart. Thank you.'

'Then you will have to sleep here tonight,' said the North Wind, 'because it is so far that we will need an entire day to get there.'

The next morning the North Wind woke the girl up early, and he puffed himself up so much that he looked huge and terrifying. The girl climbed up onto his back and he spread his mighty wings and set off at a frightening speed. He roared over land and sea, so that forests were blown down and ships were wrecked by the blasts from his wings and from his icy breath. On and on they flew, over a vast ocean that stretched away for as far as the eye could see. The North Wind was weakening now, and he went slower and slower, and lower and lower, until he was just skimming over the crest of the waves.

'Are you frightened?' he asked the girl.

'No,' she replied, 'I'm not frightened.'

At last the girl could see land ahead, and the North Wind had just enough strength to blow all the way to the shore and drop the girl off under the windows of the castle that lay East of the Sun and West of the Moon. The North Wind had to lie there for many days resting before he was strong enough to make the journey home.

The following morning, the girl sat beneath the castle windows and played with the golden apple, tossing it up into the air and catching it again. Princess Long-nose, the troll who was to marry the prince, saw her playing with the golden apple and she wanted it.

'I want that golden apple,' screeched the troll. 'What will you sell it for?'

'It's not for sale, for gold or money,' replied the girl.

'Well, what will you have for it?' demanded the troll.

'I will let you have it if I can spend one night alone with the prince who you are about to marry.'

'It's a bargain,' said the troll, and she sent her troll servants to go and get the apple.

That night Princess Long-nose prepared a sleeping potion and gave it to the prince before he went to bed. When the girl was taken to the prince's bedchamber she saw the familiar face of her true love asleep on the pillow. She shook him and whispered sweetly in his ear that she had come for him, but he slept on. She shook him as hard as she could,

she prayed and cried out to him to wake up, but it was no use. She wept bitterly all night, still shaking and calling to him, but the prince slept on and didn't know that she had ever been there. The following morning Princess Long-nose came with her troll guards and threw her out of the castle.

Later that same day, Princess Long-nose looked out the window and saw the girl carding wool with a pair of golden carding-combs.

'I want those golden carding-combs,' screeched the troll, 'what will you sell them for?'

'They are not for sale, for gold or money,' replied the girl.

'Well, what will you have for them?' demanded the troll.

'Another night alone with the prince who you are about to marry,' said the girl.

'It's a bargain,' said the troll, and she sent her troll guards to get the golden carding-combs.

That night passed as the first one, with the girl crying, praying and calling to the sleeping prince.

The following day the girl sat under the castle windows spinning wool on a golden spinning-wheel. Once more, Princess Long-nose saw her and stuck her head out of the window to talk to her.

'I want that golden spinning-wheel,' screeched the troll, 'how much will you sell it for?'

'It's not for sale, for gold or money,' replied the girl.

'Then, what do you want for it this time?' demanded the troll.

'A third night alone with the prince who you are about to marry,' said the girl.

'It's a bargain,' said the troll, and she sent her troll guards to get the golden spinning-wheel.

That day, the prince was walking around in the castle and he happened to talk to some Christian folk who the trolls had carried off to the castle. They were staying in the room next to his, and they told him that for the last two nights they had heard a girl crying, praying and calling to him all night long. That evening, when Princess Long-nose brought him his night-time drink, he guessed that it contained a sleeping potion, and he threw it over his shoulder when the troll was not looking and pretended to sleep. When the girl was let into the prince's bedchamber he was still lying as if in a deep sleep, but when she touched his shoulder he sat up and gazed at her.

'You have found me,' said the prince, and they hugged each other lovingly.

'You have come not a moment too soon,' said the prince, 'as tomorrow I was to marry Princess Long-nose, but now that you are here, my own true love, I will marry no other but you. You are the only one in the world who can set me free of this spell. I will say that I want to see if Princess Long-nose is fit to be my wife, and I will only marry the one who can wash the three spots of tallow from my shirt. This is only a job that a Christian can do, and they don't know that you were the one who dropped them there in the first place. Princess Long-nose and her pack of trolls will have no power to wash it away, and then I will ask you to try.'

And so the girl and the prince spent the night together in each other's arms, and the girl told him of her adventures and they talked lovingly to each other all night long.

The following day, the prince went to his stepmother, the witch, to talk to her.

'Now I want to see what my bride is fit for,' said the prince.

'Oh yes,' said the witch, 'what do you want?'

'I have a beautiful shirt that I want to wear to my wedding, but it has somehow got three spots of tallow on it. I have sworn that I will have no other bride than the one who can wash the stain from my shirt. If she can't do that one thing, then she is not worth having'.

'That should be no problem,' said the witch, and she called for Princess Long-nose.

No matter how hard the troll princess scrubbed and scrubbed, the three spots would not shift; in fact, she only spread the stains further and further.

'Let me try,' said his stepmother, the witch, and she scrubbed the shirt, but the stains spread all over the shirt and became blacker and blacker.

All the other trolls took a turn, but the shirt became as black as coal, and more and more ugly as the washing went on. At last, the prince shook his head and said to them:

'There is not one of you worth having as a bride. Why, look out the door, there sits a beggar girl; I bet she can wash better than any of you.'

The prince called to the girl to come in.

'Can you wash the stain from this shirt?' asked the prince.

'I don't know,' said the girl, 'but I'll try my best.'

The girl had no sooner started to wash the shirt than it became as white as snow.

'Here is the girl who I will marry,' declared the prince.

His stepmother, the evil witch, grew so angry that she swelled up with fury until she burst. Princess Long-nose was also so enraged at losing her husband that she too burst, along with all the horrible trolls who lived in the castle.

The prince took the girl in his arms and kissed her.

'You have freed me from this evil spell, and now we can be married and live together for the rest of our days.'

The first thing that they did was to release all the poor Christian folk who the trolls had carried away to the castle. Then they gathered together all the riches that the witch and the trolls had in the treasury, and they went as far away as they could go from the castle that lay East of the Sun and West of the Moon.

the two sisters

I found this story in a collection of Faroese folk tales that was published in Chamber's Journal in 1886. I had bought the book in a second-hand bookshop in Kirkwall many years ago when I saw that it contained these stories, plus another tale from Shetland. The theme of this story is a popular one, and is found throughout the Nordic world.

There was once a farmer who married a beautiful wife. She was kind, thoughtful, hard working and sweet-natured, and together they had a daughter who was as bonny and good as her mother. But tragedy struck the farmer, because, when the little girl was only a year old, her mother died and left him alone to bring up the baby. He wept for his wife, but he was also aware that he should try to seek another wife, to keep house and look after his baby girl. He met a woman who had none of the qualities of his previous wife: she was ugly, cruel, lazy and mean-spirited. Together, they had another baby girl, but this child took after her mother, which was a great pity.

The years rolled by, and the two girls grew up to be big girls. There were only about two years between them in age, but the youngest was ugly and skinny, while the elder girl was pretty and healthy. The stepmother hated the farmer's elder daughter, but she adored her own, horrible child. She beat the elder girl at every possible opportunity. Even if it was her sister who had done something bad, she would be blamed and would be punished for it. The farmer was too much of a coward to stand up to his nagging wife, and so the abuse went on, year after year. The stepmother also made the elder girl do all the work around the house. She cleaned the cowshed every winter, ground all the corn eaten in the house, picked and

carded all the wool, and spun it into thread, along with a dozen other jobs every day. In the summer she was sent to work in the fields, and she had to go up to the mountains and milk the cows every morning and evening, and all the while her half-sister sat inside by the fire doing nothing, but demanding everything.

As the years passed, the elder girl bloomed into a very beautiful young woman, with snow-white skin and rose-red cheeks. She was the very picture of loveliness, and she was kind and gentle, just like her mother had been. Her younger sister, on the other hand, grew uglier and more bad-tempered with age, and she was a sickly, pale colour from staying indoors all the time. Her mother gave her all the best things in the house to eat, and she never did any work. The elder daughter worked as hard as a slave, and only got the leftover scraps of food to eat, but still her beauty shone like the sun. Her stepmother grew more and more envious of the girl's good looks, as it made her own daughter look even more like a troll. She decided that she would spoil the girl's beautiful appearance by starving her. That night she got no supper, just a scolding and sent to her bed hungry. The poor girl went on her knees by the side of her bed and prayed to God for pity, and she prayed to her late mother and asked her to help and protect her from the miseries of life. The next morning she got no breakfast either, but was sent to the mountains to milk the cattle. The girl wept as she trudged off to milk the cattle, because she was so hungry.

After she had walked for a long time she sat down and cried, and the hot tears rolled down her beautiful face and splashed on the ground. She was so hungry and tired, and her life was made such a misery, that she wished that she could be with her own dear mother once more. Suddenly, she saw a sight that made her heart stop for a moment, for the hillside opened, and inside she saw a great chamber with a table laden with food and drink. She prayed to God for guidance, and she slowly stepped forward towards the table. The food looked so good that her mouth watered at the sight of it, but who did it belong to? It would be wrong of her, hungry as she was, to steal food from someone else; but, oh, it did look so good. Then, to the girl's surprise, she heard a voice that spoke to her. It was a woman's voice, soft and kind.

'Eat your fill, my little dear, eat!'

The girl sat down at the table and ate her fill of all the good food that was piled there. She ate things that she had never tasted before, but had seen her half-sister and stepmother enjoying. She ate her fill, and then she thanked God for the meal, and she went up the mountain to milk the cows.

Every day after that, the girl found the hill was open and that the table was always set for a feast. Every morning and every evening, when she went to milk the cows, she would find it all ready and waiting for her, and that kept her alive. Her stepmother was furious, because instead of becoming skin and bone, she now looked more beautiful than ever. Her half-sister guessed that she must be getting food from somewhere, and she would nag her sister to tell her where she got it from. The elder sister would only say that any food that she ate was not taken from her or her mother, but still the younger sister kept nagging her until her sister told her about the grand feast

that was set out for her inside the hill. She was now pleased that she had got the secret from her sister, and she decided that she wanted to enjoy the feast too.

The next day, the younger sister went to her mother and said that she would go to the mountain and milk the cows that day. Her mother was shocked, but she would refuse her daughter nothing that she desired, so she set off with the milk pail. Sure enough, there stood the hill wide open and a table piled high with the best food imaginable. The girl ran inside and stuffed the food into her mouth like a hungry troll. After she had finished, she burped loudly and walked away without saying as much as 'please' or 'thank you', because those were two words that never crossed her thin lips. That night she didn't eat a thing, as she was saving her appetite for the following day's feast. The next day she said that she was going to go and milk the cows, and she set off without breakfast or a bite to eat while she was away. When she got to the hillside she found to her horror that it was closed. She cursed and screamed in temper and stomped all around it, calling it names, but no door could she see. When she returned home she declared that she would never go to milk the cows ever again, and she sulked for days on end.

The elder sister once more had to milk the cows every morning and evening, but the hill was never closed to her, and she thanked God for the food after every meal. Now the wicked stepmother had to come up with another plan to ruin her step-daughter's good looks. The poor girl's clothes were nothing more than a bundle of rags, and she had no shoes to wear on her feet. Her stepmother chuckled to herself when she saw the girl dressed in even worse rags than the poorest beggar who called at the house looking for a bite to eat. The poor girl was ashamed to be seen in her tattered clothes, and she was cold, because there was hardly enough cloth left to cover her. She went back to the hill for her food, but she wept many bitter tears because she was so cold and ashamed by what she was forced to wear. Suddenly, she heard the same soft, kind woman's voice speaking to her.

'Take these clothes to wear, my little dear.'

And with that, a beautiful dress was handed to her. The girl stared at the dress in amazement, for it was the most beautiful thing that she had ever seen. It was pale blue, with threads of silver running through it so that it seemed to shimmer when she moved. Hurriedly, the girl put on the dress and rushed outside so that she could see it better. She sat down in the field and admired the dress; she had never been happier in her whole life than she was at that moment.

While the girl sat there dressed in her beautiful gown, the king's son happened to be riding by with his men. He saw a girl all finely dressed, and he rode over to see who it was. When the young prince saw the beautiful girl his heart skipped a beat, and he fell deeply in love with her. He asked her who she was and where she lived, and she told him, and they talked for a long time. Eventually, the prince could contain himself no longer, and he went down on one knee and asked the girl if she would marry him. She said that if he still felt that way about her in a year's time, then he should go to her father and ask him for her hand, and that she would not be inclined to refuse him. The prince rode away with joy in his heart, and the girl went home. When she arrived, wearing the beautiful blue and silver dress, her step-sister screamed with envy and tore the dress off her back and stole it. Her stepmother did not try to stop her, because she hated the girl with all her evil black heart.

A year passed by, and one fine summer's day the prince rode into the courtyard of the farm, dressed from head to toe in golden clothes, and with him rode his servant who was also dressed in the same manner. The prince introduced himself to the farmer and his wife, and said that he had met their daughter the previous year as she sat in a field, in a beautiful blue and silver dress, and that he wanted her for his bride. The stepmother was delighted, and rushed off and locked her step-daughter away in the strongroom, and dressed her own daughter in the fine dress and took her to the prince. The prince recoiled in horror when he saw the ugly, skinny girl, and he said that, while it was same dress, he had never seen the girl before in his life. The stepmother was quick-witted when it came to evil, and she said the girl had suffered from a terrible disfiguring disease, and that was why she was unrecognisable. The prince felt pity for her, and he asked that she come outside to talk to him alone. As they walked from the house the prince asked her, in God's name, if she was truly the girl that he had met the previous year, and the girl said that indeed she was. No sooner had the lie passed her lips than the girl gave a scream, swelled up and burst asunder. The prince returned to the farm. The anger rose in his heart, and he demanded to see the girl he had met, or he would have them all killed. If they lied to him again, then they could go outside and see for themselves the result of such tricks. The eldest daughter was released and taken to the prince, who gave her a golden gown to wear, and they rode off together to be married. Her wicked stepmother was full of sorrow for the death of her worthless daughter, but was so full of anger, envy and hatred that soon afterwards she died. When the old king died, the prince became the ruler of the entire kingdom, and the girl who had been so poor became the queen, and they lived long and happily together for many, many years.

Anna Anglemark

the witch's horse

The theme of this story is found throughout the Nordic countries. The belief that witches could ride people at night like horses is common in Scandinavia and in Iceland. It was believed that if a person grew sick, tired and listless it was because they were being ridden like a horse whilst asleep by a witch or 'hag', which gives us the name 'haggard'. An earlier term was 'hagridden' or 'hagrid', which will be well known to fans of a certain boy wizard.

In the neighbourhood of Östrel there was once a fine large farm that was owned by a wealthy farmer and his beautiful wife. A young man called there looking for work, and the farmer and his wife were happy to employ him. The mistress looked on him with a glad eye, and she promised him that he would never be short of good food to eat. The man was happy at first, and the mistress was as good as her word as he was given creamy porridge, cheese, bread, herring, meat and vegetables to eat. The young man had never eaten better in his life before, and he counted his blessings that he had found such good employers.

Time passed, but, despite the good food, the young man did not thrive. He grew thinner and thinner every day, until his clothes hung on him, and his strength left him and he became as weak as a child. Every day he grew weaker, until he thought that he was going to die. He decided to seek the advice of a wise man who lived in the area, to see if he could figure out what was happening to him. He knocked at the door of the wise man's house, and was greeted in a friendly fashion by the old fellow.

'Come in my boy, come in and rest by the fire. You look tired, and as worn out as an old shoe.'

'That's the problem,' said the young man.

'That's what has brought me here. I am working as a servant at your neighbour's farm, and the mistress gives me plenty to eat, but I am getting weaker instead of stronger, and thinner instead of fatter. What is wrong with me?'

'Ah!' said the wise man, 'I think I can tell you why you are not thriving, and if you don't heed my warning, you will surely die before too long. You see, my boy, the mistress of the farm is a witch, and she uses you as her witch's horse'.

'Witch's horse?' said the young man, 'What do you mean, witch's horse?'

'I will tell you,' said the wise man, 'if you'll let me. Every night, at midnight, while you are asleep, your mistress comes to you and turns you into a horse. She then rides you all the way to the church at Troms in Norway, and back again. Every night you make that journey. In the morning you remember nothing about it, but it is wearing you out. If you don't stop her soon, you will die.'

The wise man rose from his chair and hobbled over to a shelf that contained bottles of coloured potions, and took a jar of white cream and brought it over to the young man.

'Here,' he said, 'take this cream, and at night

before you go to bed spread some of it onto your head. It will cause you to itch, and will wake you up during the night. Then you will see the truth, for you will be outside of Troms church, just as I have told you.'

The young man thanked him, then, summoning up the last of his strength, he wandered off back to the farm.

That night, before he went to bed, the young man took the jar of cream and rubbed some of it onto his head, and in no time at all he was fast asleep. At midnight, the mistress slipped silently into his room and walked over to where he lay. She held a horse's bridle in her hand, and she slipped it over the young man's head. In a flash, the young man was transformed into a horse, and the mistress jumped up onto his back and spurred him on to ride to Norway. On and on he rode, so fast that it seemed that he was flying through the air, but all the time he knew nothing of it. At last, they arrived at the church at Troms, and the mistress jumped down and entered the church.

All of the time that this was going on, the young man was completely unaware that anything was happening. As far as he knew he was still tucked up in bed asleep. But then, his head started to itch. He still didn't wake up, but then it started to itch even more, and he scratched it. The itch became worse and worse, and he scratched and scratched at it until he woke up. To his amazement, he was standing outside the church at Troms with a bridle in his hand. He had scratched so hard that he had pulled off the bridle, and so the spell was broken and he returned to his human form. Next to him stood several horses, all tied together by the tails. There he stood for a long time, waiting for his mistress to come out of the church.

Eventually, he saw his mistress slip silently from the church. When she saw him standing there in his human form she smiled sweetly at him. He smiled back, and beckoned to her to come over, which she did. When she got near to him he pulled the bridle over her head, and

she was transformed into a beautiful mare. The young man jumped onto her back and rode her back home. On the way he stopped by a blacksmith and ordered him to nail horseshoes on to the mare's feet, which he was happy to do. On and on they rode, back to Denmark, the mare sending sparks flying from her new horseshoes.

After a long journey, they arrived back at the farm where he had worked. It was morning, and the farmer was out and about, inspecting his property. He had no idea what had been happening, nor that his wife was a witch. The young man rode up on the fine mare and greeted him warmly.

'Good morning,' said the young man cheerily, 'what do you think of my fine new mare?'

'She's a grand looking animal,' said the farmer. 'Would you be interested in selling her?'

'I'd gladly sell her to you,' said the young man, and they agreed a price.

As soon as the young man had the bag of money in his hands he ran back to collect what few things he had and left the farm as fast as he could. The farmer was still admiring his new mare when he left, but when he took her into the stable and took off the bridle the mare changed back into his wife. The man stood there in shocked silence, and his wife cursed and tried to pull off the horseshoes that were on her hands and feet, but they wouldn't come off. The farmer then realised what had been going on, and that his beautiful wife was, in fact, a witch. He drove her out of the farm, and she wandered off to find a new life for herself. It is said that, for as long as she lived, she still had the horseshoes fastened to her hands and her feet as a reminder of her rides to the church at Troms.

the fiddler and the trows' foy

This story I have heard my good friend, Lawrence Tulloch, tell, and he has published it in his book of Shetland stories, The Foy. It came from his father, the renowned Shetland storyteller Tom Tulloch, and shows (if proof were needed) how stories are passed on from one generation to the next. It is a local story for Lawrence, as it takes place in his own native island of Yell. I would never have dared to use it if it was not for the fact that Lawrence gave me his blessing. I hope I do it justice. 'Foy' is the Shetland word for a party or celebration, and the trows are known to be great lovers of music and are always keen to lure a fiddle player into their mounds to play for them. 'The Owld Yul Een' of the story is Yule Eve (Christmas Eve), calculated by the old-style Julian calendar, which is now the 4th of January.

Shetland is famous for its fiddle players, and rightly so. Music is in the blood, and the fiddle is regarded as the finest instrument, while good players are considered to be worth their weight in gold. Robbie Anderson, of Cullivoe in Yell, was one such fiddle player. While he and his wife and their three children were poor people, scratching a living from the soil and the sea, they were as rich as kings when it came to music. Whenever there was a wedding or a foy, Robbie Anderson was the first to be invited. Without Robbie's fiddle playing, the event was considered a poor affair, as he was regarded as the best fiddle player in Yell, if not in the whole of Shetland.

One Owld Yul Een day, Robbie was walking down a path, on his way to feed his animals, when a small man with a shock of red hair came tripping over to him. Robbie knew all too well that this was a trow that was walking towards him, and he was gripped with a feeling of dread, because the trows were best avoided if possible. They can bring about ruin and death if they are annoyed, and Robbie had heard plenty of stories about them that made his blood run cold. When the trow reached

Robbie on the path he stopped to speak to him.

'Robbie,' said the trow, 'I have come to ask if you would play for us at our Owld Yul Een Foy tonight.'

'I'm sorry,' said Robbie, 'but I can't. You see, tonight I will be going to visit neighbours with my wife and bairns, and I will be playing all night for as long as the drinking and dancing lasts. I would play for you any other night, but not on Owld Yul Een'.

'So, so, Robbie,' said the trow, 'I hear what you're saying, and I understand the position that you are in. But just you think about this: if you do come and play for us tonight, you will be well paid for it. If you do change your mind and decide to come to our home, you must keep it a secret. You must tell no one: not your wife, not your bairns, not your best friends; nobody must know about this.'

With those words, the trow vanished into thin air, leaving Robbie standing alone on the path with a head full of worries. He had never been paid for his playing before; not so much as a crooked copper penny had changed hands in

all his years of playing. In fact, it had never occurred to Robbie that he could be paid for what he did. He also knew that it was not wise to offend the trows, or his life could be made even more difficult than it was already. In fact, it could be downright dangerous to bring their hostility to bear on him or his family. And there was his wife to consider. If he couldn't talk this over with her, what would she think if he was to slip away from her tonight? What would she tell his friends and, worse still, what sort of a reception would he get on his return? Robbie trudged on down the path, a worried man.

That evening, Robbie put his fiddle under his arm and silently slipped away from his home. His heart pounded in his breast as he walked towards the mound where the trows lived. When he reached the great mound he saw that there was a door standing wide open in the side of it, and a bright light shone from it that dazzled him. From inside the mound he could hear the sound of voices and laughter, and the clinking of glasses. He walked over to the door where he was greeted by the same red-headed trow that he had met earlier in the day.

'Come in, Robbie,' said the trow, 'and be welcome'.

The trow led Robbie into a large room that had a long table that was covered with all sorts of fine food and drink.

'There's plenty of good things to eat, Robbie,' said the trow, 'so don't be afraid to eat and drink your fill. There is a corner over there where you can stand and play.'

Robbie looked at the food, and was amazed by what he saw. There were all sorts of meat, fruit, bread and cheese, and drinks that smelt lovely, but a lot of the things Robbie had never seen before in his life. It all looked so tempting, but Robbie remembered hearing stories from the old folks about fiddlers who ate the trows' food and drank their honeyed ale. After they returned home they found to their horror that a few hours with the trows

was in fact a hundred years or more, and their family, and everyone they knew, was long dead. Robbie put his fiddle to his chin and started to play. The trows danced and cried out with delight as the music flowed from the fiddle like a crystal-clear stream. There were trow men and trow women, and tiny trow children, and they all danced and skipped happily to the music. His fingers flew over the strings, and he played like he had never played before. To his amazement, he found himself playing tunes that were strange to him, and all the while the trows danced and made merry. Robbie played on all night, until eventually the trows started to leave and only a few remained to dance in the middle of the floor. The morning light was in the sky, and Robbie started to walk towards the door. To his dismay, he was not offered any payment for his playing; in fact, he never received as much as a 'good-night' or a 'thank-you' from the trows.

Robbie returned home an unhappy man. No reward, and no warm welcome for him when he reached his own door.

'Where have you been?' shouted his wife when he entered the door 'Oot,' he meekly replied.

'Oot! Oot!' yelled his wife, 'I'll say you've been oot; all night too. We were worried sick. Where have you been?'

'Oh, I had things to do.'

'What sort of things did you have to do that took you away from your family on Owld Yul Een?' demanded his wife.

'Oh, just things that I had to do,' said Robbie, still too scared of the trows to give up his secret.

'And does she have a name; this thing that you had to do?' said his wife, with fire in her eyes.

'What do you mean?' said Robbie, 'I wasn't with another woman. I would never go with anyone but you, my dear.'

'Then just tell me where you've been all night.'

'I can't,' said Robbie, 'but you must believe me, I had to go.'

Poor Robbie had a miserable time for a while with his wife. She wouldn't speak to him, but when she did speak, Robbie wished that she had not bothered, because it was never warm or loving. So time passed, and January drew to a close, and things started to return to some kind of normality in the Anderson household. But, with the closing of the month, the snows came. A blizzard so severe that no one could remember another one like it, gripped the islands in its icy claws. The snow fell, and the people were forced to stay inside until everything was covered in a deep blanket of snow. Eventually, the snow stopped, and a hard frost took a hold of the islands. The sun shone like a cold yellow gem in the sky, and there was not a breath of wind to ripple the surface of the sea.

Robbie's neighbours suggested that they set off and go to the fishing. Robbie agreed, as he was keen to have some fresh fish to eat instead of salted mutton. They pulled on the oars and rowed until they reached their fishing grounds, and then they drifted as they threw out their baited hooks. Before they knew what had happened, the lines began to tighten and to jerk downwards, and to their delight they pulled in a fine catch of fish. No sooner had they put more bait on the hooks and thrown them over the side than the hooks were full of fish. None of them had ever experienced fishing like this, and they hauled fish aboard all day until the boat could hold no more. They headed home with a record catch of fine, sleek, fat fish, as it was spawning time and the fish were heavy with roe. They ate their fill that evening, and they divided the fish among all their neighbours so that everyone could enjoy their good fortune. The next day the frost still bit hard, so they returned to their fishing grounds and enjoyed the same success as the day before. For days they fished, and every day they caught so much fish that they were able to supply all their neighbours with a large quantity of fish to enjoy fresh, or to salt for later. One day, Robbie didn't go to the fishing with them, as he had work to attend to on the farm. Without Robbie, the men didn't enjoy the same success, and only a few fish were caught. The following day, when Robbie returned with them, they had the same luck as before. There were so many fish that they didn't even bother baiting the hooks, as the fish greedily seized them without the need of an incentive.

Robbie started to wonder if this was the payment that the trow had mentioned. Whatever he did, he enjoyed great good luck. When the snow melted, the crofters went out into the hills to look for their sheep, fearing the worse. Many men lost a lot of their sheep, up to half of the flock in some cases, but Robbie didn't suffer a single loss. That spring every ewe had twin lambs, and they had plenty of milk to feed them with. As the summer passed, Robbie enjoyed great success at the fishing, while his crops grew like never before. Everything that Robbie did was a success, thanks to the trows. If proof was needed that the trows were helping Robbie, it came that autumn, when a severe gale blasted the crops in Yell and left them flattened and broken in the fields. All, that is, except for Robbie's oats. His crop was untouched by the wind, and it produced so much grain that he was able to buy another cow.

When it was Owld Yul Een again, Robbie took the same path that he had taken the previous year in the hope of meeting the same trow. Sure enough, there was the small red-headed trow he had met before, and he invited him to come and play for them again that evening. This time, Robbie agreed right away, and was reminded that he was not to tell a soul about where he was going or what he saw. He slipped away quietly from his house and went to the mound, where he found everything as it was the year before. He played all night, and left without a word of thanks in the morning. This year, his wife said nothing, because she had guessed what he must have been up to, and she had seen the change in their fortune as a result. If anyone else knew, they said nothing, and Robbie continued to enjoy the best of luck and to prosper.

The years passed, and Robbie played for the trows every Owld Yul Een, and his luck and his fortune grew. His children had grown up and left home, and they were all enjoying the blessing that the trows had bestowed on them.

One Owld Yul Een, Robbie set off as usual to walk along the path where he always met the trow, but this year no trow came to speak to him. He returned home, wondering if he had got the time wrong, and he set off a bit later to see if the trow would come to him. Still no trow appeared, and he spent the whole day pacing back and fore along the path, but there was no invitation to play for the trows. That evening he wondered what he should do. Eventually, he took his fiddle under his arm and walked to the trows' mound, but it was a very different place this year. There was no sound of voices and laughter, and no clinking of glasses. Robbie stood there in silence, and had just decided to return home when he saw, far off in the distance, a small glimmer of light. He walked into the open mound and headed towards the light. There, in the corner of the room, sat an ancient old trow woman, huddled over a few glowing peats. She looked at him, and said in an old croaky voice:

'Thank you for coming, Robbie, but you will not be needed here any more'.

'Why?' asked Robbie, 'What has happened to everyone? Why are you not celebrating Owld Yul Een this year?'

'They've all gone, Robbie,' replied the old trow woman. 'They've all gone away over the sea.'

'But why?' asked Robbie.

'There's a new minister here in Yell,' said the old trow woman, 'and he hates us trows. He prays that we will all be driven away, and he preaches against us to whoever will listen. The trows have had enough of his preaching, and they've all gone away to live in the Faroes.'

'But why didn't you go with them?' Robbie asked.

'Because I am too old and frail,' replied the old trow woman. 'I couldn't stand making that long journey, and this is my home. Anyway, I'm kind of deaf, so I can't hear the minister's preaching.'

Robbie said farewell to the old woman and headed for home.

His wife was surprised to see him return that evening, but they went to visit their neighbours as they had done in the old days, and Robbie played his fiddle as they drank and danced. No more would Robbie play for the trows, and without them on the island his luck returned to that of a normal man. Some things worked well for him, while other things didn't. But he was a wealthy man now, and he never had to scratch a living from the soil or the sea again, thanks to the luck of the trows.

Anna Anglemark

the miser's ghost

There are different versions of this tale in Iceland, which is famous for its ghost stories. It was believed that misers would hide their wealth and then haunt the site, as they could not bear to be parted from their money.

There was once a wealthy farmer who lived in a fine big farm in the north of Iceland. Although he was rich, he never gave a single penny to the poor, but instead he hoarded his fortune away in secret and no one got any use out of it. His wife, on the other hand, was a generous person, but, despite her goodness, none of it rubbed off on her miserly husband.

One winter, the farmer became ill, and after a short while he died. His body was washed and dressed in a shroud and a fine coffin was made for him. The funeral was a quiet affair, for he didn't bother much with friends, as he thought them an extravagance that he could live without. A grave was dug for him in the churchyard, and he was laid to rest by a small band of mourners who had come out of respect for his wife. The widow, who was still a young and attractive woman, started to settle his debts and to put the farm's business into order, but she could not find any money. People asked her where all the money had gone, but she said that she had never seen a penny of it, and there was no sight of it now. Her neighbours knew that she was as honest as the day was long, and it was whispered that the farmer must have buried his fortune so that no one could enjoy it after he was gone.

The winter passed by, as it always does, but things at the farm started to go bad for the widow. It became clear that the farmer's ghost had returned to his old home in order to be near his money. The haunting grew worse and worse, until the servants started to leave. By springtime, the widow had hardly any servants left, and she knew that it was useless for her to try to keep the farm. She had decided that it was coming near the time when she would have to sell-up and leave.

One day, a man arrived at the farm looking for work, and the widow was only too happy to hire him. He was a good worker, and the farm's fortunes started to take a turn for the better. After a short while the man became aware that the farm was haunted, and he asked the widow if her late husband had buried any money around the place, but she could only say that if he had, then she did not know where it could be.

The summer turned to autumn, and it was time for the local market. The farmhand went into town and bought himself some white linen cloth and some sheets of tin, which he brought back to the farm. He cut out the cloth and made a shroud for himself and, being a skilled tinsmith, he made a breastplate and a pair of gloves from the sheets of metal. The farmhand waited until the nights had grown long, and the darkness spread over the land, and then he fastened the breastplate to his chest, put on the tin gloves and covered them all with the white linen shroud. When everyone was sleeping he slipped silently from the house, and headed down to the churchyard. He stood there, alone and cold among the dead, and he took out a silver coin and started to play with it. He knew where the miserly farmer was buried, and he paced back and fore by the side of his grave, waiting. After a short time, the ghost of the farmer rose up from the grave, and he fixed the farmhand with a cold, hostile look.

'Who are you?' asked the miserly farmer's ghost. 'Are you one of the dead, like I am?'

'Yes,' said the farmhand, 'I am one of the dead, just like you'.

'Let me feel you,' said the farmer's ghost, and the farm worker held out one of his hands. The farmer's ghost could feel how cold and hard the hand was.

'Yes, you are a ghost all right,' said the farmer, 'your hand is as cold as the grave. But why do you walk the earth? What brings you back here?'

'I have returned to play with my silver coin,' said the farm worker.

The farmer's ghost looked at the small silver coin in his hand, and he threw back his head and let out a shrill, hollow laugh.

'You poor wretch,' said the farmer's ghost, 'if only you could see how much money I have to play with!'

'Do you have a lot of money?' asked the farmhand.

'Oh yes,' said the farmer's ghost, 'I have a lot of money indeed!'

Suddenly, the farmer's ghost turned around and ran out of the churchyard, followed by the farmhand. They ran and they ran until they reached the farmer's old home, and they went to the edge of a field near to the house. There was a small mound there, and the farmer's ghost kicked it over to reveal a hidden cash box. The farmer's ghost opened it, and the gold and silver coins glinted in the moonlight. The box contained a fortune! The farmer's ghost started to play with his money, and the farmhand joined in. They tossed the coins up into the air, and showered themselves with riches. All night long the two of them played with the money, but eventually the farmer's ghost wanted to put it all back into the cash box.

'You can't put it away yet,' protested the farmhand, 'I've not played with the small coins yet,' and he scattered them on the ground in front of him.

'Are you sure that you're dead?' asked the farmer's ghost.

'Feel for yourself,' said the farmhand, and he held out his other hand for the ghost to grip.

'Yes, it's true,' said the farmer's ghost when he felt the other tin glove, 'you are one of us.'

The farmer's ghost started to gather together all the coins, but the farmhand went on scattering them over the ground. The farmer's ghost grew angry, and he screamed at the man.

'You are no ghost! You are one of the living trying to betray me!'

With that, the farmer's ghost grabbed the farmhand by the chest, but he felt the cold, hard sheet of tin that covered the man's front.

'Truly, you are as I am,' said the farmer's ghost, and he carried on gathering up his money into the box.

The farmhand knew that it was dangerous to anger the ghost any further, and so he left him to gather up his money and put it back in its box.

'Do you know what I would like to do?' asked the farmhand.

'No, what would you like to do?' asked the ghost.

'I would like to put my silver coin in with your money,' said the farmhand.

'You can do that if you wish,' said the ghost, and so the farmhand dropped his coin into the cash box with the ghost's riches and then they both returned to the churchyard.

They arrived by the side of the farmer's grave.

'Where is your hole?' asked the ghost.

'Oh, it's away on the other side of the

graveyard,' replied the farmhand.

'You go into your grave first,' demanded the farmer's ghost.

'No,' said the farmhand, 'you go in first'.

The two of them argued for a while until the cock crowed and the farmer's ghost jumped into his grave and vanished from sight.

The farmhand returned to the farm and took off his shroud, and the iron gloves and breastplate, and placed them in a wooden tub full of water that he hid under the landing. He then went out to where the cash box was buried, and he dug it up and carried it back to the farm and placed it in the tub with the other things. He made sure that everything was completely covered by the water and then he went to bed.

The next day the farmhand said nothing about his adventures the previous night, and he just went about his business as usual. As night fell all the people on the farm retired to bed, while the farmhand made a bed for himself opposite the door. The night was far advanced when the ghost of the farmer opened the door and came into the room, sniffing at everything. The farmhand watched him as he went around the room sniffing, searching for his cash box. If the farmhand had not covered it with water, then the ghost would have smelt the earth on it and discovered where it was hid. The ghost was furious when he didn't find his money, and he smashed his fist against the side of the landing before leaving the farm and returning to the churchyard. Quickly, the man jumped from his bed and followed the ghost back to his grave. He knew a thing or two, that farmhand, and he used all of his skills to fix the ghost in his grave so that he would no more be able to walk the earth and bother people. Once he had dealt with the ghost, he returned to the farm and went back to his bed.

The following day the farmhand took the widow to a quiet room and he told her what he had done. She looked on in amazement when he brought out the cash box, and she gasped in wonder when he opened the lid to reveal the dead farmer's hidden fortune. She thanked the farmhand for everything that he had done for her, and her gratitude turned to love as the weeks passed. After a while, there was a wedding celebrated at the farm, when the widow and the farmhand were married. They had a grand wedding feast, with plenty of food, drink and laughter, and those were things that they never lacked in the years to come.

the widow's son and the fairy princess

The following story is from the island of Lewis in the Hebrides, or Western Isles, as they are also known. When the Viking Earls of Orkney ruled the Northern Isles and the North of Scotland, they also claimed control over these islands, which they called the Sudreyjar, or Southern Islands, as that was the viewpoint from Orkney. Kings of Norway also laid claim to them, but today they are very proud of their Gaelic language and culture. The name of the hero in this tale was given in Gaelic as Domhnull Donn, meaning 'Donald Brown' (possibly from the colour of his hair), while his companion's name was Alistair Beag, meaning 'Little Alistair'. The home of the fairies is called Cnoc-nan-sithean, meaning the 'Hill of the Fairies'. I will use the English names in this telling, to avoid confusion.

It was a stormy midwinter's night as Donald Brown and his friend, Little Alistair, walked home by Fivig Bay, laughing and joking together. The two young men were around twenty years old, and had been good friends since their childhood. Little Alistair, as his name implied, was a short but strong man, with dark hair and eyes, while Donald Brown was tall, handsome, and with auburn hair and blue eyes. Donald lived with his widowed mother and his sister, and was regarded as a very fine fiddle player. As they approached the Hill of the Fairies, they could see its dark shape silhouetted black against the stormy night sky; it was a place that most folk avoided after dark. Suddenly, to the two young men's astonishment, the side of the hill split open and a piercing light tore the dark night's sky and illuminated the land around where they stood. They stopped dead in their tracks, transfixed by the sight that met their eyes, and then, softly at first, they heard it – the loveliest enchanting music that flowed from the inside

of the hill. They stood there spellbound, listening to the strange music that filled their senses so that they could think of nothing else but its beauty. Donald was the first to speak.

'This must be the night when the fairy folk hold their great dance,' he said. 'I have often heard the old folk tell of how the fairies gather to celebrate midwinter with music and dancing, but I never thought that I would ever get to see it. I must have a closer look, as this may be my only chance to see the fairy folk playing their instruments, and I greatly desire to see what it is that they play on. I'm going to have a look inside the hill.'

'You will do no such thing,' replied Little Alistair. 'Let's get out of here as quickly as we can, because this is no place for mortal men to be. The air seems to be filled with spirits, and I fear for our lives if we stay here a minute longer.'

Alistair grabbed Donald's arm to prevent him from approaching the hill, but Donald just tossed him aside as if he had been nothing more than a sheaf of corn, and he ran towards the light. Alistair watched in horror as his friend's form became a black silhouette against the intense light that streamed from the mound, then suddenly the opening closed, and Donald was gone.

Alistair stood there shaking, and blinded by the sudden darkness that now engulfed him, and, when his eyes grew accustomed to the night once more, he ran as fast as if the hounds of hell were at his heels all the way to the home of Donald's mother. He burst in through the door, gasping for breath, and told the old woman all that had happened, and how Donald was trapped in the Hill of the Fairies. To his surprise, the old woman didn't seem too concerned.

'My boy is a Christian,' she said in a calm voice, 'and as long as he doesn't renounce the faith of his fathers, then they have no power to injure him. Keep this quiet, Alistair, and in a year's time, at the very same hour at which you saw the Hill of the Fairies open, we will return there so that I can call to my son to come back to us. I have no fear that he will be safe and well, but we must wait for another year.'

When Donald walked up to the door of the Hill of the Fairies, he was greeted by the most beautiful young woman that his eyes had ever seen. She wore a dress of emerald green, and her long golden hair hung down her back like spun silk.

'Welcome, son of the widow,' she said to Donald.

'Do you know me?' asked Donald.

'Yes,' she replied, 'we know of you, and we know of your great love of music. We have much to teach you here in my father's hall, if you have the desire to learn.'

'Oh, that I do,' replied Donald, 'but I beg of you, keep the door of the hill open for me, so that I might return.'

'Look behind you, son of the widow,' said

the fairy princess, and when Donald looked behind him, he saw to his horror that the door was closed.

'Don't be afraid,' said the fairy princess, 'for we mean you no harm. You are the first mortal who has had the courage to enter our realm, and that, and your love of music, will keep you safe'.

The fairy princess smiled at Donald, and her sapphire blue eyes sparkled with warmth and kindness. 'Come, son of the widow, and join in our dance'

'Oh, I couldn't do that,' protested Donald, 'for I am dressed in rags and not fit to be seen in your company."

'Look to your right,' she said softly, and Donald saw his reflection in a polished crystal mirror. He saw that he too was now dressed in green, with a green cap, and a sash of pale blue over his left shoulder.

Strangely enough, Donald was not the slightest bit alarmed by this sudden and unexpected transformation, and he was led by the arm into the hall by the fairy princess.

The hall was so magnificent that it took Donald's breath away. The room was oval in shape, and the great domed ceiling, that was as blue as the sky, rested on arches that were supported by pillars of blue and white marble. Between the pillars were painted scenes of the local landscape that Donald recognised, particularly one of Fivig Bay lashed by a storm in the moonlight. The floor was of polished Jasper, and over it glided dancers who were all dressed in green. At the one end of the room was a small platform, covered with green cloth, where forty musicians played on fiddles and harps. To the left of the musicians was a great double door, the top half of which was covered with green cloth. The hall was lit by chandeliers that held globes that were filled with a strange, soft green glow that cast an even light over the hall and produced no shadows. By the walls there were benches that were upholstered with green cloth, where some of the fairies sat and talked to each other. In the air seemed to hang a sweet perfume that added to the enchantment of the place.

'Dance with me,' said the fairy princess.

'I can't dance,' said Donald.

'Then I will teach you,' said the fairy princess.

When Donald put his arms around her waist he found himself silently gliding around the floor, just like the other dancers. He danced with the fairy princess for a while, and then she took him by the hand and led him to the great double doors.

'I am going to introduce you to my father and mother,' whispered the fairy princess.

When they reached the doors, they silently swung open for them to enter, like they were opened by invisible hands. They then entered another room where two people sat at a round, green table. Donald knew that they must be the king and queen, and he bowed low before them. The king had long, flowing golden hair, like his daughter, and a beard of the same colour, while the queen had long auburn hair, and in her bearing she possessed all the grace and elegance of a queen.

The king received Donald's greeting kindly, and signalled to him to be seated on the bench on his right.

'Sit down, son of the widow. May I congratulate you on your courage in entering my realm, where no mortal man has ever set foot before.

'You are known to us, as is your family, and we know of your deep love of music.'

The king took a bundle of green cloth and unwrapped what was inside. It was a beautiful green fiddle, inlaid with silver and mother of pearl, and he held it out to Donald.

'Take it, it is a gift,' said the fairy king. 'My daughter will give you lessons so that you can be the master of this instrument, and you will be the finest fiddle player that has ever been known among your people. Your children, and their children's children, will also inherit your gift as fiddle players, and your whole family will be respected for it.'

'Thank you, sir, for this most generous of gifts,' said Donald, 'I will treasure it always. I hope that I can fulfil the faith that you have placed in me.'

'Don't be afraid of that,' said the king, 'for my daughter will teach you much about this instrument, and we fairies always mean what we say. We don't waste our time on lies like mortal men, but rather we live by four guiding rules of life, and those are Reason, Truth, Justice and Equality. I am the king of this underworld realm, and all the fairies respect me and are obedient to my word, yet I dress the same as them and live in the same style and eat the same food. What I want for my people is exactly the same as what they desire for themselves, so we live together in peace and harmony. In your world there is selfishness, cruelty, greed and murder, all things that are alien to us.

'Your kings live in great luxury, while their people live in poverty. Your mother is a poor widow who wears rags and often goes hungry, while your minister lives in grand style, dresses in fine clothes and eats the best that there is to offer. He makes promises of a better life after this one, and yet his actions could not be further removed from those of the founder of your faith.'

Donald had never heard such sentiments uttered before, and his face flushed red and his voice trembled as he made his reply.

'But your majesty, there must be superiors and inferiors in society in order for law and order to work. Without such things, there would be chaos.'

'Do you really think so'?' asked the king. 'Here in my realm, I am the superior, as you would say, and yet I don't need to be different from my people by dress, home or table. I live as they do, and yet they respect me and are obedient to me. Do you see any chaos here?

'Where are the murders and robberies that your people are used to?'

Donald had no reply to the king's words, and the king saw that the young man was embarrassed, so he brought the conversation to a close.

'Go now with my daughter and she will teach you how to become a master fiddle player.'

'Thank you, your majesty,' said Donald, 'I will bear in mind the words that you have spoken to me this day.'

The fairy princess took Donald, by the hand and led him to another set of doors, which silently opened in front of them. They stepped outside of the hall, and, to Donald's utter amazement, he found himself by the side of a crystal-clear stream that ran down a slope among trees. It was nothing like the bare, rugged coast where he lived. The trees were small, but they all hung heavy with fruit, even though it was midwinter in Donald's world. The air was warm and sweet, and the sky was again a great dome of blue, with soft green lights that bathed the world in a soft, comforting glow. Brightly coloured birds, the likes of which Donald had never seen before, flew among the trees and perched on their branches. The stream bubbled and danced over rocks, and gathered in deep pools where fishes with scales of green, silver and gold swam. The ground under Donald's feet was carpeted with moss and short grass as soft as velvet.

The princess led Donald to a bower, semi-circular in shap,e that was made from willow trees that seemed to grow into one other.

Around the sides was a bench, upholstered in green cloth, and in the centre was a circular green table. The princess led Donald to the seat, and they sat by the table. There was a bowl of fruit in the middle of the table, like the ones that he had seen growing outside. There were succulent red grapes and other red-skinned fruit that Donald didn't know.

'Eat some of the fruit,' said the princess.

Donald looked at the tempting fruit, but he was afraid to touch it. The princess could see that he was embarrassed, and reluctant to eat, and she said to him in a soft, kind voice:

'They are safe to eat, you need not fear them. They will not hurt you, but in fact they will do you a lot of good. After you have eaten of those fruits, you will be on your way to becoming a great fiddle player.'

Donald took some grapes and bit into the sweet, red fruit; it was unlike anything that he had tasted before in his life. He ate a hearty meal of the fruit, and he could feel the music welling up inside of him.

'My father told you that I would give you a lesson. You have now started, and when I give you this fiddle you will be able to play anything that you like on it. You can stir all the emotions that are inside your people with your playing.'

The fairy princess took the green fiddle and played on it as Donald ate the fruit. She played a tune so complex and beautiful that Donald's heart soared with joy when he heard it. After she had finished, she handed the fiddle to Donald and said:

'You take it now, and play me that piece of music that I have just played.'

'Oh, I'm sorry,' said Donald, 'but my fiddle playing is nothing like as good as yours, and besides, I have only just heard that piece of music and could not learn it so quickly.'

'It fills me with joy, son of the widow,' said the princess, 'that it is within my power to give you the gift of being a master fiddle player.

'You do not have to go through years of practice, because I can make your dreams come true. Your great love of music means that I can give you what is in your heart – your desire to play like no one else.'

The princess took the green fiddle and she gently breathed on the bridge of the instrument, and then she took the bow and breathed on that too, and then she handed it to Donald.

'Now, play that piece of music that I have just played you,' she said.

Donald took the fiddle and started to play the same piece of music.

The sweet tones filled the air, and the bow glided over the strings as if guided by magic. He played the tune perfectly, and he could feel other tunes building up inside of him, just waiting to be released.

When he had finished, he stood up and bowed low to the fairy princess, and thanked her for the gift of music that she had given him.

'What is that tune called?' asked Donald.

'I am sorry, but that I cannot tell you,' said the faiiy princess. 'The names of our tunes are for us to know, and are secret from the mortal world.'

'Then may I be as bold as to give it a name'?' asked Donald. The princess smiled and nodded.

'Then I will call it "The Fairy Princess", if that is all right with you?'

'Yes,' said the fairy princess, smiling kindly at Donald, 'that is all right with me.'

Suddenly, the princess sat upright, as if listening to something far off in the distance.

'I think that it is now time for you to leave,' she said, 'for I think that your mother must be waiting for you.'

The princess led Donald back through the room where he had met her parents, but the room was now empty. He went through the great hall, which was almost empty, and back towards the door where he had entered. He stopped to say goodbye to the fairy princess, but then he heard a familiar voice. His mother was calling to him.

'Donald, my son, in the name of the Father, the Son and the Holy Ghost, I command you to come back to me.'

Donald bowed low to the fairy princess, who smiled sweetly and waved her hand in goodbye, and then he found himself back outside in the darkness.

Donald's mother and Little Alistair were waiting for him outside, and the old woman was shouting:

'Donald, my son, come back to us. We have missed you. Come home, my son.'

Donald rushed to his mother, saying:

'Mother, whatever is the matter? Why the fuss? I've not been away for long.'

'A year, Donald,' said his mother, 'a year, that's how long you've been away from me.'

'Oh mother,' said Donald, 'you must be losing your mind, for I've only been away for a few hours.'

'Those evil fairies must have bewitched you Donald,' said his mother, 'for you have been away for a whole year.'

'Now, mother,' said Donald, 'I don't want you saying bad things about the fairies, for they are kind and gentle creatures, and they were good to me. But you must be the one who is bewitched if you think that I've been gone for a year. See what they gave to me.'

Donald held out the fiddle to his mother, but she drew back in horror.

'Put that evil thing away, Donald,' she said, 'for you have been bewitched. Tell him, Alistair.'

Little Alistair now spoke to Donald:

'She's right, Donald, you were taken from us a year ago to the hour.

'You have been away for a whole year.'

'Come home now, Donald,' said his mother. 'Your sister and I have prayed for you this last year. Our neighbours have given you up for lost. Fancy thinking that you have only been away for hours, and coming home with that evil instrument.'

Donald knew by her trembling voice that his mother was serious, although he thought that he had only been away for a few hours. He would have gladly stayed for longer if the fairy princess had not gently led him by the hand back to the door. On their return to his home, Alistair said goodbye to them, and he returned to the bosom of his family. The words that the fairy king had spoken to Donald deeply affected him, and he was renowned for his kindness and generosity ever after. He was also famous as the greatest fiddle player that anyone had ever heard, and he was much in demand for playing at weddings, harvest homes and other occasions where folk gather to celebrate and enjoy themselves. His greatest masterpiece was 'The Fairy Princess', but no other fiddle player could ever master it. Donald did try to teach it to other players, but no one else could even master one bar of it. He only ever told his sister who had taught it to him, and he never spoke of his time with the fairies to anyone outside his family or closest circle of friends.

Donald married, and was the father of six sons. Each one of his sons grew up to be fine musicians, and the gift was passed down through the family, just as the fairy king had foretold. He lived to be an old man, but, when he died, the tune that he called 'The Fairy Princess' died with him.

the city under the sea

In this tale, the young hero is captured by a mermaid, who uses her magical powers to make him her husband. The mermaids and fin folk were always on the lookout for a human husband or wife, and with good reason. If a mermaid married a fin man she was doomed to lose her great beauty and to become a horrible-looking old crone known as a fin wife, who would make a living on land as a witch. As the mermaid was a very vain creature, she wanted to preserve her beauty if she could, and that is why she was keen to have a human husband.

Arthur Dearness lived in a small croft called Corsdale in the island of Sanday. He was considered to be the most handsome and strongest young man in all the island and, when it came to feats of strength or athletics, Arthur had no rivals. While all the girls smiled at Arthur, and wished that he would fall for their charms, Arthur only had eyes for Clara Peace, whose father owned the large farm of North Skaill to the north of Corsdale. Clara and Arthur were very deeply in love, and enjoyed nothing better than to walk the long beaches of white sand that stretch for miles along the coast of Sanday. One evening, Arthur had gone down on one knee and asked Clara to be his bride, and with tears of joy in her eyes she had accepted. He promised that he would always love her, and that he would always be there to protect her and to look after her for the rest of their days together. The wedding was planned for December, and everyone in the island thought there had never been such a fine-looking couple as they were. Happiness and joy filled Arthur's days, but that was all about to change one fateful evening in the late autumn.

The harvest had been won from the fields and was safely built into stacks in the yard of the croft, ensuring enough food to feed the cattle during the cold hard months of winter. At this time of year, the fishing can be good, so Arthur thought that he would go and gather some limpets to use as bait on his fish hooks. He walked to the shore at Hamaness with a bucket in his hand, and he selected a flat stone which he would use to knock the limpets from the rocks. He had quickly gathered a good quantity of limpets when he saw a great number of large limpets on a rock face that hung out over the sea. He lay flat on his stomach and lent out as far as he could over the sea, striking the limpets from their rocky home with a swift, sharp smack of the stone. As he worked, he thought that he could hear music: soft and gentle at first, like a whispered melody inside his head. The music seemed to grow louder, and the enchanting tune filled the air around him like a sweet, heady perfume that filled Arthur's senses until he could think of nothing else but the wondrous sound. He lay there as helpless as a newborn child, wrapped up in the sensual embrace of the hypnotic melody that danced through his mind. Then it seemed that far below him, deep under the sea, he could see a pair of sparkling blue eyes gazing up into his own ones. Those eyes captivated Arthur, and he stared deep into them as they seemed

to rise up, nearer and nearer to him. Then, before he knew what was happening, a pair of milk-white arms broke the surface of the water and wrapped themselves around his neck, and he could feel himself being drawn down into the sea, and then the light went from Arthur's eyes and he tumbled into darkness.

When Arthur woke up, he found himself lying in the bow of a boat that was travelling at speed towards the setting sun, and there was no sign of Orkney to be seen. The ocean stretched out in all directions around them, like a vast eternity of blue. In the stern of the boat sat the most beautiful woman that Arthur had ever seen. She had long golden hair that covered her milk-white skin, and the only clothing that she wore was a silver skirt that glittered like the scales of a fish. It was twisted together to form a tail, which hung over the stern and into the sea, and with this she propelled the boat. Under her skirt Arthur saw a pair of milk-white feet sitting on the bottom of the boat, as her tail was actually this strange garment. He knew that this must be a mermaid, and a panic started to rise in his breast. He thought of home, and of his lovely Clara who was waiting for him, and he could feel a cry welling up inside of him. He tried to remember the words of a blessing or a prayer which would break the spell, but the mermaid saw the danger, and in an instant she leapt forward and kissed Arthur on the lips. Arthur sat there in a daze, and then the mermaid breathed into his mouth and her breath ran down his throat like warm honey.

All thoughts of home or Clara left his mind, and all that he could think of was the beautiful woman who was there in front of him. He crawled to the stern of the boat and curled up next to the mermaid; he was now totally under her spell. All that Arthur could think of was how much he loved the mermaid; no one else, just her.

The mermaid looked up into the darkening sky, like she was searching for something. She steered the boat until she positioned it right underneath a bright star that she could see up

in the heavens, but was invisible to Arthur. When the boat was right beneath the star, she said, in a loud crystal clear voice:

'Sea, Sea, open to me!

'Open the door to Auga'.

That was the first time that Arthur had heard the mermaid's name; Auga: Then, to Arthur's horror, the sea began to rise and swell around them, and a hole opened up beneath the boat like a whirlpool, and the boat sank down into the sea. Arthur struggled, thinking that his final hour had come, but to his amazement he found that he could breathe underwater like a fish. He settled back into Auga's arms and she embraced him and stroked his hair, and the boat continued its journey down to the bottom of the sea. Out of the deep, dark water Arthur could see buildings emerging below them. There, stretching out as far as his eyes could see, was the great city of Finfolkaheem, the home of the fin folk and the mermaids. The boat glided down and came to rest gently in a great square right in the centre of the city, and Auga led Arthur out of the boat and into a great hall. In the entrance, he saw mermaids at work grinding pearls into dust between quernstones, like they ground corn into flour at home in Sanday.

Arthur was led into a silver chamber and was told to sit down while Auga went to get changed. When she returned, she was wearing a gown that shone with silver and gold, and around her neck was a string of pearls, each one as big as a cockleshell. She wore no other jewellery, as no diamonds could sparkle under Auga's eyes, as they outshone all the precious gems in the world. Arthur did see love shining from those eyes, though, and that love was for him, and him alone. She had watched him from the sea for a long time, longing to touch him, to feel him next to her, and she had fallen in love with him as she watched him from her watery realm. Now she would have him forever.

'You are in the great city of Finfolkaheem,' said Auga, 'and we are soon to be married, you and I. You will rise to be a very important man here, and you will want for nothing, and enjoy great honour among my people.'

Auga took out a golden comb and began to comb her hair, all the time kissing Arthur, who grew more and more in love with her with every passing minute.

'You must be dressed for the feast that the fin folk are holding to celebrate your arrival and our wedding. Come, put this on.' Auga took a long silk robe from a chest and handed it to Arthur to wear. Then, two of Auga's maids took off his shoes and woollen socks so that he would enter the Fin Folk's Foy Hall barefoot, as was their custom. They washed his feet carefully, and then anointed them with a sticky ointment, over which they sprinkled pearl dust so that Arthur's feet glistened in the light.

Once they were ready, Auga took Arthur by the hand and led him to the Foy Hall where the celebrations were to be held. On entering, the fin folk gave a loud cheer, and they took their seats at the high table next to the most important people in Finfolkaheem. The hall was nothing like Arthur had ever seen before in his life. The entire place, walls, floor, ceiling and pillars, was made from crystal, and it was lit by a soft phosphorescent glow that gave it a beautiful appearance. All the assembled mermaids gathered in a line, and each one kissed Arthur's feet, as the mermaids love the taste of mortal man, but Auga would not suffer any of them to kiss him on the lips. Arthur thought that the mermaids were all very beautiful, but none of them could compare with the radiant beauty of his Auga.

The doors opened, and a huge feast was brought into the hall and set on the tables for the hungry guests. There were dishes filled up with whalemeat, roasted, boiled or stewed in blubber. Other dishes contained the meat of seals and otters, and there were fish of all shapes and sizes. A pot of whale and seal soup, thickened with cod's roe, was also set on the table, and the only vegetables that Arthur could see were seaweeds that had been cooked in seal oil. There was no bread of any kind to be seen, but the food was much better than the barley and fish that Arthur usually had to live on. They did have horns filled with foaming rich ale, and bowls of blood-red wine, and every time one was finished the mermaids would fill it up again.

A very old fin man, with a beard that hung down to his middle and was tucked into his belt, stepped forward to preside over the wedding. He had a large dish containing a whole roasted great northern diver set in front of Arthur and Auga, and he took out a long knife and cut the bird in two, lengthwise, down the middle. One half was set on a dish in front of Arthur, while the other half was given to Auga.

'Now, bairns,' said the old fin man, 'you must eat all the flesh that is on this bird, and you must pick the bones clean. I will count the bones when you are finished to make sure that you have both eaten all of it, for this is the true sign of whether your wedding will be blessed with luck or not. Eat up now! Your future happiness depends on it.'

Arthur started to eat, but it was a large bird, and he was struggling to eat it all. Auga, meanwhile, seemed to have no trouble in eating her half, which made Arthur feel a bit downhearted. Suddenly, a black cat jumped up on Arthur's knee. He had never seen a cat here before, and he wondered where it had come from. He looked around, but it seemed to him that none of the rest of the wedding guests could see it. The cat stretched out its paw and took a bone from Auga's plate and ate up the last scraps from it before putting it back on the dish. It then seized the leg from Arthur's plate and started to eat that too, which he was only too happy about, as he was getting full. The cat ate all the meat off the leg bone and then put the clean bone back on the plate.

By eating a share of the wedding bird, the cat had broken a very powerful spell that was being cast upon Arthur, although he didn't realise it at the time. When they had finished the old fin man counted the bones and found them all there.

Next, the old fin man handed them a large horn that was filled with blood-red wine.

'Drink this,' said the old man, 'for this is the wedding horn. You must drink it between you, and it will make the two of you become one forever more.'

Auga drank deeply from the horn before passing it to Arthur, who raised it to his lips to drink. The smell of the wine filled his nostrils, and it smelt so good that Arthur's head was spinning. Suddenly, the cat appeared on Arthur's knee again, and it knocked the bottom of the horn with its head so that the wine spilled down Arthur's front, between his robe and skin. He was not so happy about this, and he tried once more to drink, but the cat knocked the bottom of the horn once more and again spilt the wine. Every time that Arthur tried to drink, the cat prevented him, and yet Arthur found himself powerless to prevent it from doing so. So another powerful spell was broken by the cat. The old fin man saw that the horn was dry, and declared that this part of the ceremony had been successfully completed.

After this feast, the young mermaids took Auga and carried her to the end of the hall and laid her down on a beautiful rug. The young fin men carried Arthur to another rug, and then they began to roll Auga and Arthur back and fore on the rugs; this, he was told, was to help aid digestion so that they didn't suffer any ill effects from such a large meal. Once this was over, they were led to the great Dancing Hall, and Arthur could hardly believe his eyes when he saw this wondrous place. If he had thought that the Foy Hall was beautiful, then it looked dull compared to the Dancing Hall. All along the walls of the great hall there were curtains of light, shimmering and swimming before his eyes. It resembled nothing less than the Northern Lights (called the 'Merry Dancers' in Orkney), when they are at their brightest. They shone red, blue, green, yellow, white and pink, and with the magic powers of the fin folk, they were kept in constant motion as they gently shimmered up and down. The dancing went on late into the night, and Arthur danced until his legs were sore. The ale flowed like water, and Arthur wasn't the last to accept a cog of the foaming brew.

At the end of the night, a large tub of strong drink, called the 'Goodnight Drink', was brought in and served to all there. Then the fin folk sang their traditional song, called *The Fin Folk's Foy Song*. At the end of every verse they stamped their feet on the floor, which felt as if it would bring down the roof. After that, two mermaids set Auga on a large cushion and carried her from the hall, while six mermaids led the way and another five followed. Then two fin men set Arthur on another cushion and he too was carried from the hall, with six fin men leading the way and five following. Arthur was taken into a lovely golden bedchamber, undressed and placed in the bed next to Auga. The thirteen young mermaids and the thirteen young fin men danced around the bed, then left them alone.

Arthur was rather drunk by this time, and he was also very tired. He saw what he thought was the black cat jump up onto the foot of the bed and then slip under the blankets and crawl up the bed between them, Then, to his surprise, he could feel the cat change shape until it was a huge eel with sharp teeth. He tried to put his arm around Auga, but every time his hand slid towards her, the eel bit it. Arthur cursed the eel, and tried again, but once more he was bitten, and after a few attempts he gave up. Once more, the cat broke a powerful spell over Arthur. As he lay there he thought that he could hear the eel whispering sweet nothings into Auga's ear, and then he drifted off into a deep sleep.

The next day they rose at rising time, as there are no nights and days in Finfolkaheem, and they ate their breakfast. Arthur was then taken hunting by the young fin men. They set off riding on seahorses, and they used seals and otters like dogs as they hunted all the fish in the sea. After they returned, Auga would wash Arthur's feet, and comb his hair with her golden comb, and they would sit and kiss tenderly as they lay in each other's arms. Arthur was also able to explore this strange, new undersea world. The houses were made of crystal and coral, and were decorated with colourful shells. The gardens grew seaweed instead of flowers, and brightly coloured fishes swam among them like birds in the mortal world. There was a great horn set up on a stand, and, when it was blown, that was the signal for the herds to drive the flocks of whales and sea cows to Finfolkaheem to be milked. Mermaids milked them, and the milk of the whale was greatly prized by the fin folk.

The days passed unnoticed, and Arthur lived there with his mermaid bride as happy as a lark. With no days and nights, time meant nothing to him, and all his thoughts were of the beautiful mermaid who lay in his arms. He was bewitched by her beauty, and by her magic. He never thought about his home in Sanday, nor his family or friends who lived there. He never spared a single thought for poor Clara Peace either; he no longer remembered her or the promises that he had made to her by the shore in Sanday when he asked her to be his wife.

When Arthur didn't return home from gathering limpets, his family and friends went out to look for him, but without any luck. They found the bucket of limpets that he had been gathering at Hamaness, but there was no sign of him. They thought that he must have fallen into the sea and drowned, and they searched the shore for his body, but there was not a hair of Arthur to be seen. They sent news of Arthur's disappearance to Clara Peace at North Skaill, and the blood drained from her face when she heard the news. She sat down in silence, staring straight ahead of her as if she was a corpse, and she never made a sound nor moved a muscle. Her grief was so great that she could not even cry; the hot tears that should have rolled down her bonnie face froze inside of her as she sat there, unmoving, unblinking.

Her parents decided to call for her Aunt Marion to come and see her, as she had a reputation of knowing magic. People thought of her as a spaewife, a witch who used her powers for good, and, as she lived at the house called Grindaley, she was often just called the Goodwife of Grindaley. A servant was sent to tell her the news, and she told him to return with the message that she would be with them in the morning. That night she used all of her magic skills to determine the truth about Arthur's disappearance. All night long she toiled, and in the morning she staggered from her chamber covered with sweat and weak from the effort that she had put into finding out Arthur's fate. She washed herself and took a horse to ride to North Skaill, but on her way, she stopped off at Arthur's house to see his parents.

'Do not grieve,' she said, 'for your son is still a living man yet, and if all goes well, you will see him yet.'

Arthur's parents shook their heads sadly, for they had already given up their son for dead. She then rode as fast as she could to see Clara, who just sat there as if she was in a trance.

'Take heart, my dear,' said Aunt Marion to Clara, 'for I believe that Arthur is alive, and with my powers I will bring him back to you.'

No matter how hard Marion tried, she could get no response from Clara; it was as if she had died that night too. Three weeks passed, and still there was no sign of Arthur. His friends searched the shore, but no body was ever found; it was as if Arthur Dearness had never existed. The people mourned Arthur, but no one mourned more than Clara Peace. She drifted around the house as silent as a ghost, never speaking, never smiling, and never showing any signs of her feelings.

Arthur was sitting in Auga's chamber one day in Finfolkaheem. She sat on his knee, snuggled up to his chest as he held her and tenderly stroked her hair with his right hand. She looked up at him with her beautiful blue eyes, and her love for him shone as brightly as sunbeams breaking through the clouds. She had fallen in love with him the first time that she had seen him walk by the shore, and here he was now in her own realm. Arthur smiled at her, for his love for her was as strong as ever, even though it had been won by her magic spells. Suddenly, the black cat appeared on Arthur's left shoulder, though it was invisible to Auga. It watched intently as Arthur stroked her long golden hair with his right hand, and then it pounced. The cat seized the index finger of Arthur's right hand between its paws and it drew the sign of the cross on Auga's forehead. The mermaid let out a piercing scream, as mermaids cannot stand the word of God or the sign of the cross. There was a loud noise like a clap of thunder overhead. Darkness fell over Arthur, and he dropped senseless to the floor.

When the sight returned to Arthur's eyes he found himself not in Finfolkaheem, but lying on the rocks at Hamaness where he had been gathering limpets the evening that Auga had taken him. There, standing over him, was the Goodwife of Grindaley, who smiled when he opened his eyes.

'Where am I?' he asked.

'You are home, with your own folk,' replied the old woman.

Arthur was in a daze, as all the events of the previous three weeks seemed to be swirling around in his head, but then he remembered Clara.

'Clara!' he shouted, 'I want to see Clara.'

'You will, boy, soon enough,' said the woman, and she helped him to his feet.

'It was you!' he declared. 'The black cat, that was you!'

The old woman smiled and said that it was indeed her.

'You have saved me from spending the rest of my days a prisoner in Finfolkaheem,' said Arthur. 'How can I ever repay you?'

'Come with me, Arthur,' she said. 'There is someone who would like to see you.'

Then the Goodwife of Grindaley took Arthur up on her horse and they rode to North Skaill. Arthur burst through the door and there, in a kind of trance, sat Clara. When she saw him, she cried out, and all the tears that she should have shed were unleashed at last. She wept uncontrollably as she held his face in her hands, not daring to believe that it was really him come back to her. He kissed her lips and told her that he loved her, and they both wept for joy as they held each other tightly, not wanting to ever let go.

It was decided that Arthur and Clara's wedding should be held as soon as possible to try to prevent Auga from carrying him off again. They walked to the kirk and were joined together as man and wife, and there was not a bonnier couple ever seen in the whole island of Sanday. The celebrations lasted for days, with drinking and dancing, and much happiness being shared with everyone who was there. They lived together in love and happiness for the rest of their long lives, and were devoted to each other for as long as there was breath in their bodies.

It was said that Auga haunted the rocks around Hamaness for many years after that. If you went down there in the early light of the day you could hear her song echoing around the rocky shore. It was not the enchanting song that she used to ensnare Arthur Dearness, but a heart-breaking song of loss and sorrow. Who knows, maybe she sits there to this day and sings other lost love songs to the rising sun.

91

Anna Anglemark

Sheepskin Boy

> There is a famous version of this story from Norway that was collected by Asbjørnsen and Moe. The theme is a common one, where the much-abused and ragged younger son or daughter comes through to win the day.

There was once a farmer who had three sons. The eldest two sons worked on the land with their father, whilst the youngest was given the job of looking after the sheep that grazed in the woods. He carried a ram's horn with him that he used to call the sheep, and he always wore a coat made out of sheepskin, so they called him Sheepskin Boy. One day, as he was watching over his flock of sheep, they wandered into a part of the woods that Sheepskin Boy had never visited before. The trees started to thin out, and he saw before him a mountain rise up into the sky. On top of the mountain sat a giant troll who was making pots. Sheepskin Boy blew his ram's horn to gather his sheep together, but the troll heard it and looked at him. 'That's got a fine tone to it,' said the troll. 'Would you like to swap your ram's horn for this fine fiddle that I have here? It is a wonderful instrument, because it has magical powers. If you play this fiddle, then anyone who hears it will be forced to dance for as long as the tune lasts.'

'That looks like a fine instrument,' said Sheepskin Boy. 'I'll gladly swap it for my ram's horn.'

Sheepskin Boy took the fiddle, and walked further along with his flock. He raised the fiddle to his chin and began to play, and sure enough, all the sheep started to dance merrily as they walked along. After a while, Sheepskin Boy and his flock came to another mountain, and in front of it was a lovely green meadow. Sheepskin Boy let his sheep graze on the lush green grass while he lay down to snooze in the sun. Suddenly, a huge door in the side of the mountain burst open and out of it came a huge ferocious troll.

'Who is it that dares to let his sheep eat in my meadows'? roared the troll. 'I'll eat them all for my dinner!'

'Oh no you won't,' said Sheepskin Boy, 'because I'm going to make you dance!'

Sheepskin Boy put his fiddle under his chin and he played and he played, and the troll danced and he danced, and no matter how hard the troll begged him to stop, Sheepskin Boy played on until the troll had danced himself to death. With the troll dead, Sheepskin Boy thought that he would go and explore what lay behind the door in the mountain. He walked through the door and found himself in a huge hall, so he started to look for something that he could eat, because he was hungry. He didn't find any food, but lying on top of a polished stone table there was a small box, and inside it was a whistle. Sheepskin Boy put the whistle to his lips and blew, and suddenly another smaller troll appeared.

'What do you desire, my king'? asked the small troll.

'I am not your king,' said Sheepskin Boy.

'Oh, but you are my king,' replied the troll,

'because you have killed my old king, so you have replaced him. My name is Lunkentus, and I can grant you whatever wish your heart desires.'

'Well,' said Sheepskin Boy, 'I am very hungry and would dearly like something to eat.'

No sooner had the words passed his lips, than the table was covered with all sorts of fine food. Sheepskin Boy ate until he could eat no more, then he sat back and started to talk to Lunkentus.

'I don't suppose you have heard about the beautiful princess of this land?' asked Lunkentus.

'No, what about her?' asked Sheepskin Boy.

'She sits on top of the Glass Mountain, and in her hand she holds a golden apple,' said Lunkentus. 'Anyone who can ride up the mountain to her three times will win her hand in marriage, the golden apple and become king of this country one day. Keep the whistle, and if you come back tomorrow, I can help you to win her, but you must not breathe a word about me to anyone. Do you understand?'

'Yes,' said Sheepskin Boy, 'I understand.'

When Sheepskin Boy returned home, he found that there was a great buzz of excitement in the house. News of the princess on top of the Glass Mountain had reached the ears of his brothers, and they were determined to ride up to her and win her hand.

'Oh, please, can I come with you?' pleaded Sheepskin Boy, but his brothers only laughed at him.

'You'?' they said. 'Go to win the hand of a princess? I don't think so! Look at you; you are not fit to be seen in good company, dressed in your shabby old sheepskin coat. No, you had better stay with your sheep, and not embarrass us when we ride up the Glass Mountain to win the princess.'

The next day the two elder brothers set off to try their luck riding up the Glass Mountain. Their father accompanied them in the hope that one of them might succeed, but poor Sheepskin Boy was sent off to the woods with the flock of sheep. When he reached the mountain, he took out the whistle and blew it. In a flash, Lunkentus appeared before him, and Sheepskin Boy asked him for help to ride up the Glass Mountain and win the hand of the princess. Lunkentus gave him a beautiful suit of armour made out of polished copper, and a horse whose saddle and bridle were trimmed with copper, and a bag filled with copper coins. Lunkentus also gave him a small crystal bottle filled with a magical potion.

'When you reach the Glass Mountain,' said Lunkentus, 'ask someone to hold your horse, and then go aside and drink some of this potion.

'Give the bag of copper coins to your groom, and then ride up the Glass Mountain. Do not stop when you reach the top, nor take the golden apple, but ride straight back down the other side.'

Sheepskin Boy thanked Lunkentus for his help, and he put on the copper armour and rode away.

When he arrived at the Glass Mountain, he saw his father and brothers there. His two brothers had tried to ride up the mountain, but had failed. Sheepskin Boy looked at the Glass Mountain that soared up towards the sky and he saw that there was no foothold to be had on its smooth polished sides. It looked impossible. He rode right up to his father and asked him to hold his horse for him. He looked so grand in his copper armour that his father did not recognise him, and he held his horse's reins while Sheepskin Boy slipped away out of sight and drank some of the magic potion. When he returned, he thanked his father and gave him the bag of copper coins. Sheepskin Boy spurred on his horse and it ran straight towards the Glass Mountain and rode right up the side of it, sending splinters of glass flying from it hooves. When he reached the top, he smiled at the princess, before riding straight down the other side again and away out of sight. He went back to the mountain where

Lunkentus lived and returned the armour to him, and dressed back into his sheepskin coat and linen trousers.

When Sheepskin Boy returned home that evening his brothers and father could speak about nothing else but the strange prince dressed in copper armour who had ridden up the Glass Mountain to the princess. The brothers were not undaunted, and had decided that they would once again try to ride up the Glass Mountain the following day. Sheepskin Boy pretended that he knew nothing about this, and he pleaded with them to let him join them, but they only laughed at him and said that he was not well-enough dressed to be seen in public with them.

The next day, the two elder brothers left with their father to try their luck at the Glass Mountain, while Sheepskin Boy had to take the sheep to the woods. He went to the mountain and blew the whistle and Lunkentus appeared. This time he had with him a suit of armour made of shining silver, and the horse's saddle and bridle were also trimmed with silver, and he had a bag of silver coins. Sheepskin Boy rode off to the Glass Mountain, just like the day before, and there he met his father and brothers, who had again failed to ride up the polished glass slopes. Once more, Sheepskin Boy got his father to hold the reins while he drank of the magic potion, and then he gave him the bag of silver coins. Once again, he rode up the Glass Mountain, as the splinters of glass flew from the horse's hooves like slivers of ice. When he reached the top, he smiled at the princess, and then rode back down the other side and away.

That evening the elder brothers could only speak of the mysterious prince in the shining silver armour who had ridden up the Glass Mountain, and then rode away, who knows where? Sheepskin Boy again pretended to be ignorant about it all, and pleaded to be allowed to join them the following day, but his brothers once more laughed at his tatty clothes and refused to be seen with him in public.

On the third day, the elder brothers and their father rode off to the Glass Mountain for one last try, while Sheepskin Boy was sent to the woods with the sheep. When he reached the mountain he took out his whistle and blew it and Lunkentus appeared. This time, he had a magnificent suit of armour that was made out of glittering gold, while the horse's saddle and bridle were trimmed with gold, and he had a bag of gold coins in his hand. Sheepskin Boy put on the glittering gold armour and rode away to the Glass Mountain. He saw his father and brothers, who were hurt from their attempt to ride up the glass Mountain, and he asked his father to hold his horse's reins while he slipped away to drink the magic potion. He gave his father the bag of gold coins and then rode his horse right up the Glass Mountain, sending splinters of glass flying like broken icicles. When he reached the top, the princess and her courtiers went over to him and asked him for his name, but he turned his horse to ride away. In the fuss and confusion, one of his golden shoes fell off, and he rode away back down the Glass Mountain.

The princess took the golden shoe, and declared that whoever the shoe fitted must be the true owner and that he would be her husband.

Everyone wanted to marry the princess, and they all tried to put on the shoe, but it wouldn't fit anyone. It nearly fitted one nobleman, but it was obvious that it was not a perfect fit and so he was disappointed.

Back at his house, Sheepskin Boy's brothers were talking about the mysterious prince in the glittering gold armour, and about the gold shoe that had belonged to him.

'I am going to go and try on that golden shoe,' said Sheepskin Boy.

'You?' laughed his brothers. 'Why on earth would you try on the shoe'? That is just absurd!'

But, in spite of their laughter and name-calling, Sheepskin Boy put on his sheepskin coat and set off for the castle where the princess lived.

The king and his subjects stared in amazement as the ragged figure strutted up to the princess and asked her for the shoe. She handed it to him, and he put it on. It fitted him perfectly! He took out his whistle and blew it, and Lunkentus appeared before him with his glittering gold suit of armour. When he put it on, there was a great cheer from the crowd, and the princess threw her arms around him and hugged him tightly. The wedding was arranged, and they were married with great pomp and ceremony. Sheepskin Boy loved the princess, and she loved him just as much.

Back at Sheepskin Boy's house his parents were getting very worried about him. He had been gone for weeks, and they feared for his safety. His brothers just laughed, saying that he would have either been thrown into prison by the king or had his stupid head cut off for wasting the king's time. This did not cheer up his parents, and they worried all the harder.

At the castle, Sheepskin Boy suggested that the princess should meet his family, and she was happy to agree.

'Just one thing, though,' he said, 'I want you to play along with me, for I want to have a laugh at their expense for once. Whatever I do, please don't be angry with me, but just pretend that all is normal.'

The princess agreed, and they invited the king to join them on the visit to his parents. Sheepskin Boy put on his old sheepskin coat and linen trousers and went home ahead of them.

When he walked through the door, his parents were both relieved to see him and angry with him.

'Where have you been?' asked his mother 'We have been worried sick about you, you useless scamp!'

'I got a job working in the kitchen at the castle,' said Sheepskin Boy. 'In fact, I've invited the king, the princess and the whole court to come here and visit you.'

'You've done what?' screamed the old woman, just as she saw the royal carriage roll up to the door of their house.

'What on earth am I going to feed them with?' asked the old woman.

'Boiled potatoes and dripping from the frying pan,' answered Sheepskin Boy. 'The king likes nothing better to eat than that.'

'But who will serve the king?' asked the old woman.

'Oh, don't worry about that,' said Sheepskin Boy, 'I'll do it. I have done it before; it will be fine.'

The king, the princess and all the court walked into the house, and Sheepskin Boy sat them down at the table. He took through a pot of boiled potatoes and dished up two potatoes on each plate.

'There you go, and that's all you're getting!' said Sheepskin Boy.

When he went back into the kitchen, his mother grabbed him by the hair and pulled it hard, as she was annoyed at him for being so rude to the king. He then took out the frying pan with the dripping in it, but pretended to trip up and he poured all the fat into the princess's lap.

His father grabbed him by the scruff of the neck and pulled him outside and threw him into the pigsty and fastened the door behind him. He then ran back to the house to apologise to the princess.

That night, the princess was given an attic bedroom to sleep in.

During the night, Sheepskin Boy broke out of the pigsty, and put a ladder up to her window and tapped on it for her to come and let him in. The princess opened the window and helped him to climb in through it, and they snuggled up together in bed. The next morning his father came to wake the princess, but, to his horror, he saw Sheepskin Boy lying in bed next to the princess. He frantically signalled to him, hissing between his teeth:

'Get out of there! Get out of there!'

'No chance,' replied Sheepskin Boy. 'It's nice here; I'm staying where I am."

With that, the princess woke up and started to laugh, much to the old man's confusion. The princess told him that Sheepskin Boy was, in fact, her husband, and that they were playing a trick on them.

Sheepskin Boy went outside and blew his whistle, and Lunkentus came with a fine new suit of clothes and a horse and carriage. To his parents' and brothers' amazement, Sheepskin Boy rode away back to the castle with his princess bride by his side. When the old king died, Sheepskin Boy inherited the kingdom, and he lived in peace and happiness with his beautiful wife for the rest of his days.

the author

Muir was born in Tankerness, Orkney, in 1963.
the Exhibitions Officer with the Orkney Museum,
he joined as Assistant Custodian in 1988. He
tten many books on Orkney's folk tales, folklore,
heritage and history. He has promoted the use
ney's rich folk tales in Orkney schools, which has
tended to the whole of Scotland's schools through
cational website, 'Scotland's Stories', as well as to
my and France. His book *The Mermaid Bride: and
kney Folk Tales*, published by *The Orcadian* in 1998,
n translated into Japanese and Icelandic.

l as being a writer, Muir is an internationally
ned storyteller, bringing Orkney's stories to new
ces in Scotland, the Western Isles and Shetland,
as further afield to Newfoundland, Greenland,
l, Faroes, Norway, Sweden, Denmark, Austria,
a and Hong Kong. His work as a storyteller in the
Village of Storholmen in Sweden inspired this
on of folk tales from the Nordic world; the homes
Vikings. It was the love of these stories that fired
magination as a child and he hopes that it will also
others to find the wonder in life.

as a grown up family; Danny and Josie, and has
moved to the town of Stromness where he is
up a new home with his American lady, Rhonda